Sorensen, Virginia (Eggertsen) 1912–

Where nothing is long ago; memories of a Mormon childhood. [1st ed.] New York, Harcourt, Brace & World [1963]

213 p. 21 cm.

ı Title.

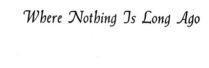

Where Nothing Is Long Ago

Where Nothing
Is Long Ago

Memories of a Mormon Childhood

Virginia Sorensen

 Harcourt, Brace & World, Inc. / New York

Dear Carol:

Writing these stories, here at home, I felt that I was speaking constantly to you. Thanks for saving that journal for me, and all those wild letters. And thanks for your memories. It's odd, isn't it, what different things we remembered? To me, as the stories grew, the wonder was as Frost described it— I remembered so many things I didn't know I knew. And—as you'll say along with everybody else—so much is "made up" it is scarcely memory at all, but a dream dreamed out of memory.

I wish I could have put more in—like the time you and Dixie prayed for a live doll, just before Marcia was born. So many people were important in our lives, your two sisters and mine, our big brothers, and I wish I could have told about your mother. But I am keeping her for a long story of her own, someday.

I see now what a paradise of space we had to live in. As one of the stories says, this is a good place for Saints to spend a millennium.

With love,

Contents

Where Nothing Is Long Ago

Where Nothing Is Long Ago

"You'll probably remember Brother Tolsen and that awful thing that happened when you were a little girl," my mother wrote me recently. Her fat script traveled the whole way around the photograph and obituary she had clipped from our Mormon newspaper. "The killing wasn't even mentioned at his funeral. All the speakers just said what a good man he always was."

Remember Brother Tolsen? I looked at his square jaw and his steady eyes, and it was as if I had seen him yesterday. Well, I thought, another one is gone; soon there won't be a real Danish accent left in that whole valley. Mormon converts from Denmark came to Utah by the thousands during the second half of the nineteenth century. Now there were only a few survivors. Not long before, it had been old Bishop Petersen himself who had died.

I was with Bishop Petersen, in his garden, the morning the Tolsen trouble happened. My mother thought I had a morbid interest in the affair, and I guess I had. It was the summer I was nine, and I was morbid about almost everything. I was absolutely certain for years afterward

3

that two piles of bloody rabbits' ears I saw on the court-house lawn at the time of Brother Tolsen's trial had something to do with the killing he was being tried for. They hadn't. They were merely tokens of the fact that the annual county rabbit hunt had gone off according to schedule.

Mother, who loves accuracy, often complains about the peculiar quality of my memories, and likely she's right. The Tolsen case, for instance, tends to get mixed in my mind with other water-thief murders I've heard of. My mother sent me a clipping about one in Utah Valley, near Provo, just last year. This man was killed with a gun, however, instead of a shovel—as Brother Tolsen killed *his* thief—and then the killer turned the gun on himself. Mother wrote on that latest clipping, "Dad and I don't see why he had to shoot himself, too. Do you?"

That's a very Western query. A poem written by Thomas Hornsby Ferril begins: "Here in America nothing is long ago . . ." and that's very Western, too. People out West remember when important things were settled violently, and they remember the wide, dry wastes before the mountain water was captured and put to use. Even now, the dry spaces, where the jack rabbits hop through the brush as thick as mites on a hen, are always there, waiting to take over; dryness hugs the green fields, pushing in, only the irrigation ditches keeping it at bay.

July was when the Tolsen trouble happened. In Utah, that's when the dry heat is most intense. Our whole valley floor is like a spot on a piece of paper when you focus the sun on it through a glass; you feel as if, any second, it is going to brown and then smoke and then burst into flame. Around it there are the quiet mountains, cool and blue, but long, dusty roads and scrubby hills lie between them and the simmering town. The river is the single link, flowing down between dusty-leaved cottonwoods from the mountains to the people in the valley.

Not that I minded heat in those days. There was no need to be hot when, on either side of the wide streets, there was cold water, brought from the river by the town's main ditch and diverted into smaller channels that ran along the sidewalks. It rushed constantly there, between banks lined with mint and grass. Wearing huge black bloomers and white pantywaists with the garters off, I spent most of my summer days in the ditches. Main Ditch was deep and lined with stones; when I skated along it in wintertime, I could hardly see over its banks. The ditches leading from it along the streets were shallow, having perhaps a foot of water in them at the peak of the spring supply.

Each household in town had its own dam—often nothing more than a couple of broad boards with a short handle nailed to them—and its own water turn when the dam was put to use. Set across the streams in the streetside ditches, and packed in with wet turf, these dams were sufficient to turn the water onto lawns and gardens, and nothing short of a calamity could prevent a householder from putting in his dam at the proper time. Every spring, the Water Master—an official of great importance in a Utah town—provided each family with a list of Water Turns, carefully worked out. We always kept our list tacked inside the door of the kitchen cupboard.

We children followed the water like pioneers, finding what dams were in and wading in the ditches where the water was highest. We kept ourselves rosy and crisp with it. Sometimes my grandmother would go with us and put her feet into the water to cool off. I recall her saying many times that Brigham Young must have been a true prophet, because he had said that Utah was The Place right in the middle of July, when nobody would think, to look at it without water, that it would ever grow a respectable bean. It was on the twenty-fourth of July that Brigham Young made his historic pronouncement, and as far as I know not a drop of rain has ever fallen to spoil the parades, the fireworks, and the pageants that take place every year on that day.

The Tolsen trouble must have been on the twenty-fifth of July, because I remember Mother's saying I couldn't wade in the grass, which was about to be flooded, unless I first collected every burned-out sparkler that had been left on the ground the night before. So, early that morning, I was busily searching the grass for wires when I saw Bishop Petersen, whose dam was in, working with the water in his garden next door. The full stream was running into it, as it would presently run into ours, for our turn followed his. His garden, like every other one in Utah, had a series of shallow furrows between the rows of vegetables, and he was damming them with chunks of turf and opening one or two at a time, so that each, in turn, received the stream. It was beautiful to see the tall green vegetables in precise lines and the moving water twinkling between them.

In half a minute, I was paddling alongside Bishop Petersen. The water in the furrows was warmer than that in the ditches, and it was glorious to feel the soft mud between my toes. And I loved to hear Bishop Petersen tell about Denmark, from which he had come as a young man. I asked him all sorts of questions to keep him talking, for his odd accent and his laughter pleased me. I recall how the robins sang and hopped down into the furrows as water darkened them and lured out long, fat worms.

Bishop Petersen said that to leave the lovely land of

Denmark one had to be very certain it was to God's Kingdom he was coming. He himself had been sure of it when he heard about the mountain water, so pure, so shining, so cold, so free. Whenever his turn came to speak at Testimony Meeting, which followed Sunday school on the first Sunday of every month, he spoke about the water. It was to him, next to the Gospel itself, the unmistakable sign of the Kingdom.

That twenty-fifth of July, he talked as usual, his white beard wobbling like an elf's, and now and then I had to turn my back to prevent him from seeing that I was smiling. He thought that, as one descended from Danes myself, I ought to know that the crisp peas I was picking and eating were *ualmindelig god* (unusually good). He wanted me to repeat the phrase, but I couldn't. The very sound of most Danish words made me giggle until I was weak. The language bristled with "g's" and "k's" exactly the way Bishop Petersen bristled with white whiskers. Yet goodness and kindness and excellent husbandry went along with all the things about him that made me laugh. I loved him dearly, as my parents did, and to most of us to be Danish—as to be Mormon—meant to be virtuous, kind, and of good report.

Mother came out to call me for breakfast, and she stood awhile, leaning on the fence, to talk. What she said and what Bishop Petersen replied is lost to me now, but while they talked, I saw Brother Tolsen coming. He ran into the yard with so urgent and desperate a look on his usually cheerful face that even I knew at once that he was in bad trouble. "Come in now," Mother said sharply to me. "The eggs will be cold already."

By suppertime, it was known all over town that Brother Tolsen had killed a man.

"But why did he hit him like that?" Mother asked my

father. "It's not like Brother Tolsen to strike anybody. Such a gentle man!"

"Twice he had turned Brother Tolsen's water off his fields in the night. *Twice!*" My father spoke with the patience of a man obliged to explain violence to a woman. "Brother Tolsen says he had no notion of hitting so hard, but he hit him with a shovel, after all. From what I hear, it struck on the edge and went over the forehead, and one eye came—"

"Finish your supper and go out to play," Mother said to me severely, and to my father, "Is it necessary to go into those terrible details in front of the children? It's enough to curdle their souls, the way you men tell it—as if you enjoyed it!"

It may seem an odd thing to remember, but I do remember that I was eating cottage cheese that night. It was made by my mother on the back of the stove and served in great bowls. Cream was poured over it, and there was a great, lovely red blob of jelly in the middle of it, from which one took a little chip of a jewel with every bite, eating one curd of the cheese at a time. It was a common summer supper. I also had a bowl of fresh lettuce, with cream and sugar, and I ate that slowly, too, leaf by leaf.

My parents said no more about Brother Tolsen until I had finished and gone outside, but I lingered on the porch in the shadows of the Virginia creepers. I heard my father say how big my ears were—". . . as big as soup ladles. She never misses a thing"—but he laughed when he said it. It was a family joke about me and my big ears, and how I was as deaf as a post when it suited me. Presently, they were talking about the killing again— how the victim's head had been bashed in and he had been found in a pool of blood near Brother Tolsen's dam.

I remember sitting there on the porch and holding my

hands up against the setting sun. Sunset was huge and red and terribly intense in July, over the western hills. Against it, I could see my own blood shining red through my skin. Heads were brimful of blood, too—I knew that from nosebleed and from teeth coming out, and from the time I hit a stump and went over the handlebars of my bicycle square onto my skull. The man Brother Tolsen had killed was not very well known to me, probably because, as Grandmother remarked, he had "fallen away from the faith" and didn't often come to church. Now, losing the faith, I knew, was one of the greatest of sins, but murder was worse; it was the greatest sin of them all. And Brother Tolsen I knew very well indeed. He was important in our Ward of the Church, and I had often heard his testimony at meeting, just as I had heard Bishop Petersen's, and in the same delightful accent. In fact, he was so good a speaker that I had heard him more than once making sermons at funerals.

I liked funerals very much then, and I find them rather stimulating now. The philosophy I learned as a child made death more fascinating than terrible. The first corpse I ever saw was the mother of one of my grade-school friends. She had died in childbirth. I had received fresh cookies from her hands a day or so before, but now she lay exactly like Snow White, like one dreaming in a lovely bed, with an infinitely small and doll-like child in the crook of her arm. I stood and gazed at her with awe and admiration.

After that, I went to every funeral remotely connected with anybody I knew. They were never forbidden to me. The corpses of men and women alike were always dressed in pure white, with bright-green aprons cheerfully embroidered to look like the fig leaves of the Garden of Eden. It was perfectly reasonable to me to believe that, as I was assured, they had just stepped "through the veil between earth and heaven." It seemed to me that they were always much handsomer than they had ever been in life, in their common house aprons or in their overalls stained with manure. I pictured them, in their clean new clothes, walking slowly westward with the sun and vanishing in a tremendous scarlet smile of sunset. I had even seen something like that in the movies, so I suspected that the miracle happened not only in Utah but also in California.

When Mother told me I could not go to the funeral of the man Brother Tolsen had killed, I was devastated, especially because there were rumors that Brother Tolsen himself would attend. He had been in jail a few hours and then had been released to attend to his work until the trial. He had a big family and a farm, and goodness only knew, people said, what would happen to them if he had to spend the rest of the summer in the jail.

"But Mother—" I cried, over and over.

"No! Absolutely not!" she said each time. She knew full well, of course, that I had a morbid interest in seeing a corpse with its head bashed in, and also that I wanted to enjoy the spectacle of a man going to the funeral of someone he had knocked headlong "through the veil" with a shovel.

In the end, I was not only forbidden to go, I was even given a neighbor's baby to tend, and in agony of spirit I saw Mother and Dad and Grandmother and just about everybody else in town go marching off to the dead man's house. No sooner were they gone, however, than I bundled the baby into his buggy and pushed him rapidly to that street. There I could at least see all the people standing around in the yard silent and serious, and I thought I might catch a glimpse of Brother Tolsen coming or going. Back and forth I walked, back and forth, pushing the buggy in the heat, envying the people as they filed slowly into the house and slowly out again after viewing the remains.

And then I really did see Brother Tolsen. Walking with his wife and oldest son, he passed so close to me on the sidewalk that he would have brushed against me if I had not drawn the buggy quickly off onto the grass. He nodded to me but did not smile, and I thought he appeared much as he always did when he went to church. People looked down at their shoes as he entered the dead man's gate, but when he moved along the walk toward the house, many stepped forward and greeted him. Between the gate and the porch, he must have stopped to shake hands twenty times. The front door opened and he went inside, and I found myself standing with my stomach pressed against the fence to watch. I could hear a breeze of comment among the people nearest me.

"It won't be easy for him to see Lena today."

"She knows it was an accident."

"But how can she believe her own husband would steal water?"

Presently, Brother Tolsen and his wife and son came out of the house. This time, he did not pause to shake the hand of anyone, but walked quickly from the yard. Then the door of the house remained closed for a while, and most of the people started toward the church, a few blocks away. When Mother and Dad and Grandmother came out of the yard, I began to push the buggy toward home, but I turned back as soon as they were out of sight. The hearse and a leading car, filled with flowers, were waiting in front of the house, and nobody was going to deny me a sight of the coffin.

I heard someone say "Poor Lena!" and the door opened again. Lena is still, to me, a vision of total sorrow. She leaned forward as she walked after the coffin, doubled over like a person with a violent stomach-ache. She was dressed in heavy black, with a black veil, and I think now how hot she must have been on that blistering day. After she had been carried off in a car that followed the hearse, the people who were left went away, and the whole house and yard looked empty and bedraggled. I walked back and forth, staring in. On the path, just inside the gate, lay one red rose, but I only looked at it. I wouldn't any more have touched it than I would have stirred my finger in a pool of blood.

Poor Lena! I knew that since her husband had fallen away from the faith she could never get much glory in the next world. Even if he had not been a water-thief, he wouldn't have done her much good in heaven. In the Mormon Church, every man can aspire to some sort of ordination—every small boy of any virtue whatever is a Deacon and can go on to be a Priest and an Elder and a Teacher and a High Priest and all sorts of important-sounding things. But a woman has no Priesthood and must depend on her husband to take her to The Highest Degree. I visualized dazzling marble steps stretching up and up to the throne of God Himself, with winged people arranged thereon according to their just deserts.

Not once, as I recall, did I think Poor Brother Tolsen! The two figures are clear in my mind. Brother Tolsen had looked sad but very straight and dignified as he walked into the house where the corpse lay, shaking hands with his Brethren as he went. Sister Lena, stooping and wild, had hidden her face in her handkerchief as she was led away. Later, I heard some talk of "poor Lena," who was "young yet, after all" and "should marry a real believer," but after the funeral I never laid eyes on her again, though I often rode my bicycle past her house, and looked and looked.

The next thing I remember about the Tolsen case is walking after school with my best friend, Carol. We went

past the courthouse, where we knew the jury was being selected, and there were those great piles of bloody rabbits' ears on the courthouse lawn, being counted. The
hunters were always divided into two teams, and the
losers had to give the winners what was called a Rabbit
Supper. I learned later, with relief, that they did not
eat the ears, or even the jack rabbits, but had chicken
pies at the church, cooked by the women of the Relief
Society. Nevertheless, those piles of ears I see to this day.

That night, there was talk at our supper table, and on
the porch afterward, about how difficult it had been to
find jurors "without prejudice." The trial itself lasted
only three short afternoons. At home, it was discussed
freely, and the talk consisted mostly of repeating what
character witnesses had said. There had been no witness
to the killing itself, and Brother Tolsen had given up at
once to the authorities: first to his Bishop, which was
entirely proper in all eyes, and then—in company with
Bishop Petersen—to the sheriff. As for Lena, she did not
come to the trial at all, but was said to have disappeared
into that vast place where there were yellow streetcars,
blue-coated policemen, a shining capitol building, and
a merry-go-round in Liberty Park—Great Salt Lake City.

Almost all that was left to be done after the character
witnesses were through was to hear the simple story told
by Brother Tolsen himself and repeated in the town with
nods of understanding and respect. His friends and neighbors considered him innocent of any real wrongdoing,
and in this the jury soon concurred. I remember Dad
repeating the words of somebody who had been very
important at the trial—probably Brother Tolsen's lawyer.
"If a thief enters a man's own house in the night and
means to rob him of all he has, all his clothing and all his
food, thereby meaning to take the very lives of his wife

and his little children—then what shall that householder do? Would his actions be judged as malice aforethought? Is it not true that he who steals water is stealing life itself?"

It was a joyful thing for Brother Tolsen's friends to see him at home again, and they have all been safer because of him. There has been no water-stealing that I have heard of in that valley since.

One other memory remains. I recall an evening, months after the trial was over, when my parents and I were driving along the road where his fields lay and saw Brother Tolsen working with the little streams that were running among his young corn. Dad and Mother waved and called to him. He lifted an arm to answer, and I saw that he held a shovel in the other hand. "I wonder if he bought a new shovel," I said suddenly.

For a minute, the air seemed to have gone dead about us, in the peculiar way it sometimes can, which is so puzzling to a child. Then Mother turned to me angrily. "Don't you ever let me hear you say a thing like that again!" she said. "Brother Tolsen is a good, kind man!"

So until this very hour I never have.

The Darling Lady

The first time I was aware of something special about Mother was on a Sunday. Barely old enough for school, yet I began that day to feel a new presence in the air. My father's tenderness came to have a meaning and I began to perceive the direction of his gestures of love.

It was one of those blazing days when nothing helps, even lemonade and whirling fans and blinds tightly drawn first to the east and then to the west as the sun moves. Some of our neighbors escaped to the mountains after Sunday school, and my sister Helen and I watched enviously as they carried out their picnic baskets and fishing rods and drove away. In Utah, among the mountains, one can arrive at another climate after an hour or two of climbing, even in midsummer. But we could only gaze at the cool blue peaks, for Dad must work even on the sacred Day of Rest. As Brigham Young always said, the railroad is an immoral institution by its very nature, its engines hooting gaily as it rushes by the sober people in their go-to-meeting clothes. To us, the only difference from weekdays, before we were old enough for Sunday school, was that we had a later dinner. Dad came home at three, not six, so dinner was about half past three instead of at noon; we had only bread and milk at late Sunday bedtime, with great squares of cheese.

About five that particular Sunday, Dad said from among his piles of newspapers, "Why don't we go up to that band concert in the park? It'll be cooler."

The park. The band. The siren mountains vanished from our horizon and left not a trace.

Mother sat up on the couch where she liked to rest after dinner. "That's a lovely idea," she said. "We can take a few things and eat on the grass."

A picnic besides. We began to dance.

"But I should have known sooner. We'll need some things."

Helen cried, "We can get them at The Corner."

Stores should not be open on the Sabbath. But this one, no more than a small shed perched at the corner of our block, was never really closed. Nor, for that matter, ever really open. Nobody was there when you went in. Mother sent us rather often for a loaf of bread or a cake of yeast, little things that are apt to be forgotten on a Saturday shopping list. "Run down to The Corner and get it," she would say, and give us her little purse. There was no street to cross, so there were no admonitions. For a long time I thought the little shop was actually named The Corner, and was surprised when I learned it had once had another name on the sign over the door. It looked bigger than it actually was, having one of those false fronts a few feet higher than the roof; winter and summer, smoke wandered over this toward the sky, haphazard blue smoke from no visible chimney.

Whenever we went in, a bell on the door tinkled. Then a distant voice called, "Yes, yes, I'm coming!"

It was a voice deliberately oversweet, like the voices of women being polite at a party. And when she came in to

serve us, the sweet voice came from a smile we instinc-
tively knew was forced. She called us "darlings" in almost
every sentence she spoke to us. "Well, well, darlings,
and what will it be today?" When we told this at home,
Dad laughed. "All the people who trade with her are
her darlings," Mother said.

So it became a family thing to speak of The Darling
Lady down at The Corner. When one of us was called
from another room, we often answered with an imitation
of that dripping voice. But then we had dozens of imi-
tations, some funny (we thought) and some, I see now,
rather cruel. We mimicked poor Davey Wright, who
stuttered, and Minnie Fox, who giggled at everything,
no matter what, in a high and helpless way. We imitated
Mother when she scolded, too—she was always comical
because she somehow could not manage to scold as if
she really meant it. We were always imitating the wife
of the solemn judge who lived on the next block. Her
Danish maid worked now and then for us and reported
that the Lady Judge was simply too genteel. When her
eldest son, a tall boy already in high school, did something of which she disapproved, she would say, "My
dear boy, if you do not behave"—and she would wave
her thimble finger, armed with a fine gold thimble—"I
shall have to give you *three* thumps—one, two, three!"
With each count she would thump gently on his forehead, and we also thumped away, weak with giggles.

But the Darling Lady was the oddest of all. When
the bell tinkled, she came through a dark-green curtain
hanging over a door behind the counter. She came like
a small, soft mole appearing gently in the grass. She
never appeared suddenly, and was always blinking, as
if really emerging from the dark. In what deep strange
recesses she led her life, behind that curtain, one could
only imagine. But her mysterious existence there trou-

bled us, sometimes, and we asked each other, "Where are her *folks?*" When we asked Mother, she said they must live in another town.

"Yes, and what will it be today, darlings?" she would ask, peering over the counter, pressing her hands upon it. There was a downy fuzz on the delicate thin skin on the backs of her hands.

That Sunday it was bread for sandwiches, and pickles, and potato chips. And mustard. This time we had a list. She read the items with profound attention and provided them with slow ceremonious motions, laying everything on the counter in a row, very neatly. Nothing could have been more different from the brisk efficiency of the clerk at the regular grocery store.

"And will that be all?"

Helen was a year and a half older than I was, and could even read the list by herself. "Yes, Ma'am," she said.

The lady touched each thing then, lightly with her fingertips, writing tiny figures in a column on her roll of wrapping paper. Then she stood murmuring over the result as if she might be reading a poem to herself or perhaps making a little prayer. When she announced the amount we owed her, she always did it tentatively, with a look that seemed sorry that it had to be so much or that we must pay at all.

We always handed her the purse, and she counted out of it with ceremony, naming the coins one by one as if she were teaching us their names. Perhaps she was. As she finished her incantation that particular day, the bell suddenly tinkled, and there, as if magically summoned, stood Mother. She had been running. She looked flushed and hot.

For a second I thought we had done something wrong. How could we have failed and how could Mother know already? The row of things still stood on the counter.

"Those pink cookies, the jumbles—isn't that what they're called, the huge ones? I forgot; we'll want something sweet at the last. And peanuts too. In the shells. There's a game we play with them."

The lady stood looking at Mother, her hands spread again on the counter, supporting her. "You are going on a picnic? Not to the canyon?" she asked, and her voice was surprisingly anxious, as if she were asking whether we were going around the world in a balloon.

"No, it's too late for that. We're just going to the park," Mother said.

The jumbles were in a big glass jar and had the brightest pink frosting I ever saw. As the lady took them out, one by one, she said to Mother, "I'm glad you're not going to the mountains. It's dangerous on those rough roads." She stood looking at Mother, one of the cookies arrested in mid-air, in her hand. Did you know I lost mine?" she asked in a low voice. "It was toward the end for me, but they wanted me to go. We went on wagons then. I didn't know any better."

Whatever could she mean? Yet Mother seemed to understand and made the clucking sound women always make when they feel sorry or disgusted about something. It is odd that I can remember even what she wore that day, a white dress with a wide belt; her sleeves were rolled up above her elbows, her collar lying open because of the heat. Her hair was coal black, and her eyes were dark brown, and I thought she was the most beautiful creature in the world. "I've only begun this time," she said with a laugh. "Can you tell already?"

"It's a look on a woman's face; I can always tell," the lady said. "And then, your husband—"

"Imagine!" Mother said. "He always tells people right away."

The lady turned and began slowly scooping peanuts

into a brown bag. We often imitated her slowness, too, and watching her now we could hardly keep from bursting into laughter. Mother knew; she frowned at us and shook her head. Then she took the purse herself and began to count out the money. When the lady handed over the bags, she said, "It's a good thing if a man is pleased."

It was because of this mysterious exchange, I suppose, that I noticed the delicate touch of my father, lifting Mother tenderly from the grass with his two hands grasping hers. "Here!" he said once, leaping up when Mother moved the basket. "You should let me do that." When I wanted to see the band over the heads of the crowd, he lifted me to his shoulder, and Mother looked up and said, "What an elephant! It's time she stopped being the baby."

The bandstand stood among trees, a platform on which folding chairs and music stands were set in a double semicircle. All of the musicians had red coats and little red caps with golden cords on them. When they began to play, the horns shone brightly in the light of white globes looped above them like strings of beads. A canyon breeze came down as we listened, as it always did in the evening, and all the leaves trembled over us, in time—it seemed to me—with the wailing of the horns.

By then the picnic itself was finished, and the quilt spread on the grass had been shaken free of crumbs. But the game was still to come, for it was played in the dark. We had played it often enough in our own yard at home, but here, in the little piece of the park we had staked out for our own, it was far more exciting. Dad had hidden peanuts, while we covered our eyes, as one hides colored eggs at Easter, behind trees, under the corners of the quilt, tucked under the handle of the basket, even by the bridge that led over Main Ditch, flowing along the street beside the park. It had a delicious cool music of its own, that ditch, and along its banks the grass was longer and greener, and the peppermint mixed with it gave its fragrance up to us when we trod on it with our Sunday shoes. We searched, laughing and shouting. Mother called now and then, "Now don't any of you fall in!"

The two of them lay on the quilt, together, looking up at the trees. They always rested after supper, lying on a couch at home which we thought had a special name. "Esther," we called it, because Dad always said, "Now we will go and see Esther." I was in school before I knew that he really said "siesta" and not "Esther" at all.

That night, as always at home, we kept running off and returning to report to them. We counted our findings, making piles of peanuts at each corner of the blanket.

"You've not found every one yet," Dad said every time. "There are *two hundred* altogether." He lay with his face at Mother's neck, and barely turned when he spoke to us. "Maybe you didn't look on the other side of the bridge?"

Once, when I came back to my pile to add some peanuts and count what I had, Mother was saying something about the Darling Lady. "When I went for those cookies, she said you told her. How did you happen to do that? She's so odd— Did she tell you about losing a baby, toward the end?"

"I didn't tell her. Not that I remember. She was coming out the other day when I passed, and I just said hello."

Mother's voice was lazy and contented. "Anyway, she says she knows by my face. Maybe it's true that there's a special look." And she added: "I didn't even realize she had been married. Did you?"

"Yes, I knew. She's one of those—" He noticed me

just then and lifted his brows and said, "Here's Little Pitcher," and asked me how many nuts I had in my pile.

Those *what?* It was something they didn't want me to hear. *Those.* It was years before I asked and was told that the poor Darling Lady was one of the polygamous wives left over when the Manifesto ended the public practice of what was called Celestial Marriage. She was given the little store to maintain herself when her husband died; the first and legitimate wife apparently divided the estate. It always seemed a shame to me that she never inherited First-Wifeship during her husband's lifetime, the way Sister Carpenter did. For years she had lived alone, on the same block as Brother Carpenter and his first wife. The day the first wife died she simply rolled her clothes into a bundle and moved in before the corpse was even moved out. The housekeeping hadn't a hitch between one and the other, a great blessing for Brother Carpenter, everybody said. Even if the second wife never had a chance to cut the first wedding cake, she helped her husband cut the one provided by the State of Utah for his centennial.

But the poor Darling Lady missed out on all the advantages. After that Sunday, I always felt this; she was of the mysterious Those over which my mother clucked her sympathetic tongue. As the hot summer changed into chilly fall, I remember going on occasional errands, and when winter came in earnest, the Darling Lady appeared from a warm shining beyond the curtain. I saw firelight around the edges and wished I might ask to stand by her open fire, a thing I loved to do. But one would as soon ask to open a letter addressed to somebody else. She wore a dark shawl and hurried, trembling, to provide for our needs. I felt sorry to bring her into the chill.

"And how is Mother now, darlings?" she always asked

before we left, shivering and holding the shawl tightly with one hand.

We always said, "Fine, thank you," but were puzzled by the serious air of her question, for Mother was never sick. On the contrary, she was filled with energy and gladness and had never seemed so pretty before. Before Christmas we learned with delight that a new baby was growing inside where she had become fat and without a lap for us to sit on.

It was the fifteenth of January we were never to forget. Snow had been falling for several days, and the window sills were high with it and the paths had to be shoveled free each morning. I woke suddenly in the cold dark. Mother always raised our window a little, for fresh air, no matter what the weather. Helen was sitting up in bed. "Mother! Dad!" It was her crying that had wakened me.

There was another sound, beyond our closed door. Voices, but the sound under them was like crying, like groaning. It was terrible to hear.

"Mother! *Mother!*" I joined Helen in calling the name. A horrible creeping smell came to us, a new presence in the dark. It smelled of fear. I could not make another sound in the clutch of it. The crying ceased, but Helen went right on calling. "Mother! Dad!" But nobody came and nobody came. As we lay and waited for the answers that had never failed us before, wind blew along the window sill above the bed; snow touched the pane with sounds like sighing. We didn't dare get up and approach the bedroom door, I don't quite know why; something was too awful beyond. We simply lay, whining in a sad duet. The long, shuddering depths of my own crying I remember as if it had been last night, and the way I held my breath to listen hopefully and then began to cry again.

Suddenly there was a voice at the window.

We both sat up at once, facing the square of snowy dark, and there was a shape, a head, and from where the window stood open to the night came a familiar voice. "It's all right, darlings! She'll be all right soon. Sssh!"

We dived together beneath the quilts and lay paralyzed with listening. The Darling Lady. Nothing to fear. And yet we lay tied together in the warm bed, hardly breathing. "You'll worry her if you go on crying. Ssssh . . . Ssssh . . . Don't cry." She spoke as one speaks to a crying child on one's lap in a rocking chair. Sweetly and softly.

We made no more sound. And presently her voice faded away. And then, at last, out of the silence, we heard our door open and Father was there speaking to us in his familiar, hearty voice. He warmed and comforted us with glasses of hot milk and said we had a fine new sister. He said he had heard us cry but had been busy just then taking care of the little baby. He did not mention the Darling Lady, and neither did we, until later. When we did, he laughed and said we must have imagined that she came on such a stormy night.

But we looked at each other, knowing what we knew. Yet that night seemed far off and long ago, for our house was a special heaven, wonderful beyond belief, with the new baby in it. We ran the neighborhood with our news. Why we did not go to The Corner and tell the Darling Lady, I do not know. But we did not. We hurried home again and peered endlessly at the tiny marvel in the basket and at the crisp nurse in a white dress and white stockings and shoes. Grandmother, whom we adored, arrived the day the nurse departed, and we went with Dad to meet her wonderful panting train. She brought us oranges and grapefruit from her own trees and shells from the sea, and she slept on a couch in our room and told us stories in the warm darkness. All our friends and relations came to visit, and bright cards came in every mail. Gifts for the baby came every day, like frankincense and myrrh tied with blue ribbons. Dad brought flowers and a huge box of chocolates that Mother opened ceremoniously on her bed every evening after supper. We could each choose one piece, which we did only after endless deliberations, from variously colored scalloped cups.

It was after Mother was up and around again, looking frail and lovely in a soft pink robe and slippers edged with rosy fur, that Grandmother said one morning, "There's not enough butter for lunch." And Mother said, "Maybe you can get some at The Corner."

Helen was off playing somewhere, and Grandmother and I went together, I proudly showing her the way. I dragged my sled, I remember, though most of the big snow had melted away. But when we arrived at The Corner, the door that had always opened before to the tinkling of the bell was closed and locked. Grandmother peered into the window where ancient advertisements hung, one over the other.

"She's there," I said. "She's always there."

We knocked and knocked, and then Grandmother walked to the side of the building and looked along a narrow walk that led to a back door. From across the street, then, a passing woman called to us. "She's gone to the hospital!" Her voice had the importance of carrying news. She started across to us. "Are you a relative?"

"No," Grandmother said. "I'm staying with my daughter down the block. We needed some butter for lunch."

"Oh. Oh, I see," the woman said. "I didn't know you, so I thought—I know she has some folks somewhere." She stood shaking her head. "I live right across here, and

I was the first one to notice she wasn't here. There was milk left out Monday, and a box of bread on the step. She was sick for three days before a soul knew. They say it's pneumonia."

Grandmother nodded and sighed and made the woman-cluck of pity. We started for home in silence. Then I asked, "What's pneumonia?"

"A bad cold," she said. "Pneumonia is a cold so bad that you can't breathe at all. So be careful you don't catch one." To Mother at home she said, "No butter. The place is closed."

"Well, then," Mother said cheerfully, "we'll just have to do the way Daddy says they do over the river."

"Do *without*," I said, proud to know the words to say, like knowing the answer to a riddle. When Helen came home, I was proud to tell her the bad news about the Darling Lady.

"Maybe she got it the night she came to that window," she said, taking the words from my mind. We looked at each other. But I'm afraid we didn't think about it again. Everything at home was familiar and warm and full of delightful surprises with Grandmother there. The Corner, as the butter had been, was thereafter done without. And hardly missed.

The next summer somebody broke into the place. In the manner of children everywhere, our neighborhood mobs smashed with stones the windows of any place left vacant very long. So with The Corner. Mother and Dad said it was bad of children to do such things, and to climb in as well was even worse. "Probably after whatever stock she might have had left," Dad said.

"Poor thing, she didn't have much," said Mother. "It had got so she never had what I wanted. Milk and bread, that was about all."

"She had peanuts," I said stoutly. "And jumbles."

Autumn came. One day Helen and I and another play-mate found ourselves behind the old place as we searched for a pup that had strayed away. Every single window of The Corner was smashed, even in the back. We stopped and peered through one of the jagged panes.

There were only a few things, a tumbled bed and three or four chairs overturned. Dishes and odd bits of this and that stood on an open cupboard that had ragged curtains on the doors. There were salt and pepper shakers still standing on the table, and a crumpled cloth and a smashed sugar bowl. Dirt was scattered over everything, and mouse tolleys, and there was a peculiar smell. Dust and rust and mold. And age, maybe. There was no fire-place, after all, but only a small cookstove, the door of the firebox standing open to show a heap of ash. The stovepipe that had once hung over it was warped and rusted, hanging half out of a gaping hole in the wall. All the time, then, in that one little room. Waiting for the tinkle of the bell. How slowly she had risen from her chair, answering, how slowly she had always moved. She must have had a terrible lot of time. I felt a hollow open at the pit of my stomach and a heaviness upon my shoulders. To be old. To be alone. Only for a second, though. Not yet.

"It's not nice to look into windows!" I cried, and turned quickly away.

I began to run. Helen came running after me, panting, and took my hand. "She was *nice*," she said.

That night, we looked at the window and at each other. "Did she *die?*" I asked. "Do you think she died?"

"She was awfully old," my sister said.

Presently she added, "She really didn't say Darling to everybody. I went with Irma once and she didn't say Darling to her. I asked some other kids and she didn't say Darling to any of them. They didn't even know why we called her the Darling Lady."

So it was she became a heroine to us, a comfort on many a winter night. Sometimes we lay and pretended that she came again, and we got up and asked her in. We took her in to see the baby, and she sat by the fire, and we brought her a glass of hot milk.

"I wish we had," Helen said.

We pretended that she sat there rocking and sipping and getting her feet dry, with her slippers by the stove. "Well, darlings, this *is* nice," she always said.

The White Horse

It was my first year in school, and nobody believes I can remember it so well. But a child remembers the most exciting days of her life, especially when they are also the most exciting days in the life of the world. It happened that I was climbing a fence when the war ended, looking at a wonderful creature who seemed to be forever fighting a war of his own. He was a stallion, white as snow, and from my house I could hear him running.

That day he was as wild as he could be. I could hear the pounding of his great hooves when I came home from an errand to the bakery, and I remember how I left the bread on the porch and slipped out to have a look. Mother told us never to go near that corral, which of course made it more fascinating than ever. I went out there quite often, even when he wasn't running, just to stamp him for luck. Whoever first told me it was lucky to stamp a white horse I have no idea; perhaps it is just one of those things children naturally know. Anyway, as long as I live, I will continue to stamp any white horse I see. If I fail to do this, I actually expect a run of bad luck. It's a simple ceremony one might as well attend to, just to be on the safe side. You wet the forefinger of your right hand on the tip of your tongue and set the spot of wet on your left palm for a second. Then, quickly, you stamp the place with your right fist. It's rather like wishing on a first star, something that—at least in my time—no child would ever fail to do.

I had to climb up on the side of our pigpen to get a good look into the corral where the stallion was kept. Once, climbing up there, I ran a sliver in my hand, and that made me wonder about luck for a while. But not for long, because something nice happened right away: Mother got the sliver out with a needle and said, afterward, "You know that beaver hat you wanted? Well, you were so brave I decided you could have it."

That morning, when I pulled myself into sight over the chicken coop, the stallion stopped right where he was to look at me. He didn't stand still, ever, but stood dancing in his special way, his head tossing and his eyes looking red and his hooves beating away and his lips curled into black lumps with some of his huge teeth showing, all in a drip. He twitched all over. His nostrils were huge, flaring, and when he neighed at me a delicious shudder went from my scalp to my toes. If I fell in, he would stomp me, I thought in safe delight.

Before I even had time to stamp, he was tired of looking at me, and whirled and pounded off to the other side of the corral, thrusting his throbbing neck over the bars.

It was hard to believe he could ever be as calm as I had seen him on the Fourth of July. He walked at the very front of the parade, with his owner, Pete Thugersen, riding him. All the manure on his belly was washed off and he was pink and white and glowing, his tangled mane combed and braided with ribbons. Over his head was a huge red plume that nodded as his head nodded in time with the music of the band. He had a wonderful sideward step, like a dance, and he seemed to smile as Pete tugged at the silver bit in his mouth. Pete had made the gear himself, bridle and reins and saddle and all. They were decorated with silver and with blue turquoise, the kind Indians use to make their jewelry. Once I had watched Pete getting his horse ready, washing him and currying him and braiding his long white hair. It was wonderful to see the way Pete handled him, talking softly all the time, patting and rubbing. Ever since that horse was a tiny colt Pete had taken care of him, and nobody else on earth would have been able to go freely into that corral. Even when the stallion was mad, Pete could quiet him. And when they were together in the parade, with Pete wearing his elegant Uncle Sam suit, they were a marvel to see. Everybody clapped when they passed, and you could tell the stallion knew all about it and that he understood just how important it was to walk at the head of the parade, even in front of the band. Just behind the band the most beautiful girl in town always rode on a hayrack decorated with white netting and silver tinsel. She was always trembling a little with the motion of the horse-drawn wagon, one hand supporting her on a silvery pole, and she had a high silver crown on her head, like the Statue of Liberty, and a flaming torch in her other hand. The band played away, every tune like flags waving, and I couldn't have told which was more beautiful, the white horse or the Goddess of Liberty.

The stallion hated his pen, I thought, maybe because he remembered what it was like to walk free in front of the whole valley. Maybe, to him, it seemed as long between holidays as it did to me. And then why wouldn't he be lonely and sad and angry when poor Pete had gone away to the war? Naturally, Uncle Sam had to go. The last Fourth of July there had been nobody to ride the stallion in the parade and he had stayed right there in his corral while the band played uptown. I wondered whether he danced to the music, there alone, but I couldn't possibly miss the parade to find out.

He paid no further attention to me at all, but just pounded back and forth. He looked cold and dirty, running in smelly manure. There was no hay in his crib and the water in the trough had frozen over. Mr. Thugersen should take better care of his son's horse, I thought. Pete would never have let him be dirty and cold and hungry and thirsty.

"Soon Pete will be home—it was in the paper," I said in a whisper, knowing of course that the stallion could not hear, or understand even if he heard. And just then a door slammed and I saw Mr. Thugersen coming out toward the corral, limping, thumping his stick on the frozen ground. He lifted a hand to wave to me and called, "He's a wild one today, ain't he?" and laughed.

Once he had asked me whether I'd like to get aboard and see what I could do, but of course he was teasing me. He knew I was afraid of horses, even of mild ones. My brother Claude had a quiet old nag named King, and I wouldn't even ride *him*. Once I had tried it when nobody was around, and suddenly old King didn't seem old any more, but went tearing around and tried to scrape me off on the barn door.

It was just at that moment, while I was talking to Mr. Thugersen, that it happened. The fire bell began to ring. Mr. Thugersen stood with his head up, sharp like the stallion, listening. "A fire," he said. I saw his wife come out on the back step, her hands under her apron, listening.

I climbed down fast. Maybe I could go and see it. Oh, boy, oh, boy, I loved a good fire. Once a barn had burned in the night, right across the street from us, and I watched it from my own bed, a marvelous sight. And the Apollo Dance Hall had burned, up behind the Manti theater, and for a time everybody was afraid it would take the theater and the whole town. That fire burned for half a day, and afterward we could see the springs that had been under the dance floor, all charred and black. Engines came from Ephraim and even from as far as Moroni and Mt. Pleasant.

Before I got to the back gate, a whistle was blowing along with the bell. And another bell—the curfew at City Hall. Then a school bell. And another one. Claude came bursting out of the back door when I reached the porch, and was onto his bicycle, his legs spreading to take the seat.

"What is it?" I shrieked after him, and he yelled, "Whadda y' *think?*" just like a brother. Over his shoulder streamed the wonderful news: *"The war is over!"*

Our whole street opened like an anthill. Everybody was headed for town within two minutes, running, smiling, calling to each other, pulling on coats and hats as they ran. Our next-door neighbor, Mr. Alder, called to Uncle Al, who lived across the street: "That's the end of it, thank God!"

"May be a false alarm again." Uncle Al never believed much of anything. He played poker with Presbyterians on Saturday night. But now he slipped into the car with the Alder family and away they went. Mother came out, buttoning her gloves, her coat loose over her shoulders.

"Dad called," she said. "I'm going to meet him on the corner." Just then the strident whistle of an engine joined the bells and Mother lifted her face and laughed into the vibrant air. "The old Peavine is having its say too," she said, and suddenly stooped and swept me against

her, hard. "Think of it," she said, "now your Uncle
Tracy can come home."

Uncle Tracy was a sailor and had been on a ship that
sank. He had floated for twelve hours on a rubber mat-
tress, Grandmother proudly said.

Horses were going lickety-lickety on the street and
all the cars in town were on the move. People were em-
bracing on the sidewalks, talking, laughing, and before
we even got to Depot Street we could hear a drum uptown and a trumpet let out a blast. By the time Dad
came running up to us, the whole band was giving him
"The Star-Spangled Banner" to run by.

"I was the first to know," he said, panting. "Got it
on the wire."

Of course. It had come by magic through the air
and my father had been the first to catch it in his wonderful bare hands. They kissed over my head and it was
also my kiss; I skipped between them as we hurried
toward town. Ahead of us Mr. Thugersen hurried alone,
his stick coming down in time to the band. The poplars
along the street were whipping in a chilly wind but nobody noticed the cold. Some had come out without their
coats, running and laughing.

There had been no time to get into uniforms—who
wanted uniforms today?—so the band marched in jeans
and boots and lumber jackets, playing as it had never
played before. Over there, over there, over there! But
now the Yanks were coming home. America the beautiful! Raggedly wheeling around on the bank corner,
they marched back by the post office.

I thought of the day when I stood ahead of Mr. Thugersen in front of Brother Jensen's window, carrying
my allowance. When I bought a Liberty Stamp for my
book, he said gravely, "That's right, everybody doing
his bit." And then he said, "I got a letter from Pete

today," as if he couldn't keep this news inside of him any longer, and showed me the envelope.

"By the Fourth of July Pete will be home to ride the stallion!" I thought, and felt my heart bursting with the gladness of the whole town, of the nation and the flag I had learned to salute each morning with my hand upon my heart. Of the world as well. Over there, over there, over there. I would go and tell the white horse. Yes, the thought came, and I remember it because it was the first thing I did when I got home. How I told him I don't remember at all. Did I shout? I only remember standing on the bars of the fence and how strange and wild he looked, running in the dusk.

A few days after that we had the first Armistice Barbecue. A whole steer was cooking in a big pit the size of a grave and lined with hot stones, right in the middle of the school lot. We stood in line for bread and butter, the Mayor himself standing at a butcher's block by the pit, sweating and laughing and cutting huge slices of red meat. My bread was soaked pink with it, and I never tasted anything so delicious in my life. Ever since then I have asked for roast beef rare, but in the best restaurants it has never tasted the way it did out of that smoking pit with the band playing.

Every year after that an Armistice Barbecue was the feature of the celebration. We had an assembly program at school in the morning, then went to the town meeting in the tabernacle, sitting patiently through the long speeches with visions of red meat dancing in our heads. But the second time I stood in that line, the citizens were not laughing as before, and the speeches had mentioned sacrifice as often as they mentioned glory. I had come to wonder about white horses and first stars and all the lucky signs I ever knew. Because of Mr. Thugersen. And because of Pete. The very afternoon the bells rang and the whistles blew, another piece of news came through the air into my father's hands. He told us the next morning at breakfast. "If you can imagine such a terrible thing—and *after* they signed the Armistice. *After!*"

Poor Pete Thugersen wasn't coming home, after all.

I never told the horse or went to see him the rest of that winter. I often heard him running, but I had not the heart to go. This seems odd, for my sensitivity was not so great that I did not enjoy looking at mourners in the town funerals to see what ravishment grief had brought their faces. Actually, I saw the white horse only once more that I remember. It was the day the Old Soldier came to speak at assembly one later Armistice Day.

What he said about the war has all escaped my memory, yet I see him clearly in my mind. He stood at one end of the gymnasium, which was made into an assembly room with folding chairs, the basketball nets drawn up with ropes. Sunshine streamed through the high windows, making crisscross patterns and filled with the curlicue motions of dust. I sat in the second row and thought he looked grand in his soldier suit, his legs sort of wrapped like a mummy's. He had talked only a few minutes when it began to happen. His voice simply stopped. He stood very still, leaning forward on the table that had been set up for him, his knuckles white.

"I hope some of you children remember Pete Thugersen," he said then. "He was my best friend. We went to school in this building together. He and I used to shoot baskets together here." He looked at the nets gathered up and sunshine fell over him and he blinked, he stood there blinking. And then he began to cry. A grown man. His face went suddenly scarlet and tied into a knot. Like water bursting from a turned tap, his tears came. Then he leaned slowly forward over his hands and such a silence in a crowded room I had never heard before. And he rose up again and stood looking up into the streaming sun as if he looked into the sky. "And what for?" he cried. "What *for?* They killed him, they shot him after the peace was signed—before we knew—"

Startled and pale, the principal stood up by his chair, his hand out as if to stop something terrible from happening. But the soldier paid no attention. He gave a terrible sob. "He was a prince, I tell you!" he cried. *"He was a prince!"*

Then he turned and rushed down the aisle and disappeared.

We sat in our orderly rows, staring at our laps. Somebody laughed, but stopped as if the laugh had been hit in the mouth. The principal said at last, "We will return to our classes now," and the band broke up without playing for us to march out as it always had before.

That was the day I went back to see the white horse for the last time. Soon afterward he was taken away and I heard that Mr. Thugersen had sold him. The next summer the corral was just dusty dry and then there were only some silly ewes and lambs.

He was angry again that day, running and pounding and tossing and whirling and stamping. How did he *know?* I shivered, watching him, the northern ancients whose blood ran in my veins whispering the old tale. Kelpies rose from the bogs and warned those who must drown, those who must soon die. They were good, after all, warning people as they did. But only if you stamped them in time.

My legs felt weak and I slipped to the steady ground. The white horse rushed across the corral, snorting, and I would not have been surprised to see fire blazing from his nostrils. Quickly, I stamped him, walking backwards, and turned then, and made for the warm house.

The Apostate

Many boxes came from Grandmother, but I remember especially that one. A letter had arrived first, telling us to expect it, and for days I listened for the Salt Lake train. When I saw the mail truck on its way to the post office, I made a beeline for town to see if a slip appeared in our box. Brother Jensen always put the package slips out right away, because—as he explained once—of the "little chicks and the funeral flowers."

My father gave a railroad sniff when he heard that. "The extra trouble people would save themselves if they sent everything express!" he said. Grandmother had to explain that the post office was easier for her than the railroad, because she lived so far out in the country. Where she lived, wonder of wonders, oranges and lemons grew on trees. Right in her own dooryard. For me, until she moved to California, an orange was something you got in the toe of your sock for Christmas. But the first year she lived away, she sent a whole box, and it was brought miraculously home through flying snow.

"I am sending another box of fruit," her latest letter said. "Some oranges and lemons and grapefruit from my

trees, but also something I think the children will especially like. See that they learn to spell it before they cut
a single one—*pomegranate*. Sometimes I cut them little,
before they're ripe, just to see the lovely pattern of the
seeds inside. When they are still white and transparent
they look like a cup of pearls, as beautifully arranged as
a honeycomb. When they are ripe they are brilliant red
and shine like rubies. It is best, I think, to cut them
straight across the middle and eat the seeds with a spoon.
Watch the juice, it'll likely stain.

"Do you remember the verses about pomegranates in
the Song of Solomon? After I came in from picking
these, I looked up the Song in my Bible. *Let us get up
early to the vineyards; let us see if the vine flourish,
whether the tender grape appear, and the pomegranates
bud forth.* It goes on to speak of 'all manner of pleasant
fruits,' and that's exactly what I have here, the whole
year around. A lot better than pine nuts and sagebrush!

"Lately I've been reading the Bible a good deal. Not
for philosophy or for religion now, but just for poetry.
And sometimes I feel that poetry is all the religion or
philosophy anybody really needs, especially if some of it
is set to a tune."

One day the slip appeared in our box, and I was so
excited I almost forgot the secret combination only the
family knew. That too was part of the magic. Box 608
was on the bottom row. From straight up the pointer
had to go right to 8, left to 6, right to 8 again, and presto!
it opened. I never passed the post office without going
in and opening that box, whether there was anything in
it or not.

The slip in hand, I stood waiting at the window while
Mr. Jensen finished with all the others. I could see bits
of him through the tiny windows of the boxes, and it
seemed ages before he appeared behind the cage. He had

to ask me to come around by the door to get the package, it was so big. "You can't carry it by yourself, can you?" he asked doubtfully.

But I tried. Gladly, proudly, I lugged it home, shouting to everybody I saw that it was fruit from my grandmother in California. I set it down in front of Carol's house and called her to come and see. "Carol—guess what it's got—pomegranates! P-o-m-e-g-r-a-n-a-t-e-s."

There is nothing better than a package. "Can *I* open it, Mother?"

She stood it on the kitchen table and gave me a pair of scissors to cut the string.

There were leaves and pressed flowers on top, dry and crumbly and faded. There were shells for our collection. Grandmother was one to come home from a walk with her pockets heavy. When she visited us, we had wonderful walks. She knew the names of stones and bugs, and of birds she discovered with her binoculars. She even knew the names of weeds and would come in with an armful of purple asters and joint grass and make a bouquet that looked like nothing I had ever seen. But that day I was impatient for the fruit. "Where are the pomegranates?" I kept asking as Mother took things out, one by one, carefully.

They were in a layer at the very bottom, lying on crumpled newspaper, each with its cunning blossom end standing up. Their skins were dry and hard, as variously green and red as apples on a tree.

"Can I have a whole one?"

I wanted to cut it myself, and it was difficult to get through the hard dried skin. I got it uneven, but when it fell apart, I saw what Grandmother had meant. In little compartments the seeds lay like shining jewels.

To eat the first one with proper ceremony I went to my secret place. This was a closet under the front stairs.

A small door led into it from the hallway, a door not much bigger than was needed to shove a trunk through. A child's door. I had loved it from the moment I saw it, and the first thing I did in that closet was to read fairy stories from the Knowledge books. Rumplestiltskin came in that door. The King of the Golden River. The brave tin soldier and little Thumbelina. Every manner of princess and elf and goblin imaginable. They seemed more alive to me when I read about them in that closet. It had so many things in it that there was barely room for me to curl up on some old flour sacks Mother kept for carpet rags. Some were already full of balls she and Grandmother had rolled out of strips cut from old clothes. When there were about eight sackfuls we would take them up to the blind Danish rug weaver who lived on the canyon road. How he managed to make his rugs so beautiful I cannot imagine, but perhaps his blindness was the very reason—the rugs had a haphazard beauty of variegated colors that I have never seen the like of since. At any rate, there were always some of those lumpy bags for me to sit among. I propped them against some table boards stored in the closet for when company came and the dining-room table needed to be stretched to accommodate them. When all six boards were set into the table it would hold our family, six then, and at least eight people besides.

I kept copies of the Knowledge books, which I was reading volume by volume, from cover to cover, in a sacred pile by the window. They lay on top of a box of books of quite another kind, a set of heavy law books that my father had studied once, every evening. He had meant to return to school before his family began growing, but finally, sadly, he abandoned the books and they began a new use when Grandmother came. There was a pressed flower, a grass, a colored leaf every few pages, which seemed to me far better than the law which I had sampled and found quite unreadable.

There was a trunk too, containing things Mother was storing for Grandmother. In this were the clothes of the grandfather I had never seen, but about whom I had heard wonderful stories. He was a boy hero during the wars with the Indians in the early days of our valley, carrying messages from fort to fort on horseback with arrows flying over. Now and then I opened the trunk and fingered the heavy cloth of his best suit and looked into a little carved box containing a gold watch and some extra buttons and studs with gray pearls. Once I wound the watch, and for days afterward I could hear it ticking fearsomely away in the trunk, like a sound from "The Pit and the Pendulum." I never wound it again. That trunk seemed to me the very symbol of the grave, exuding an odor of the past and of Grandmother's mothball effort to fight dissolution.

The window of my closet was even better than the door. Outside, it was only an oblong window like any other, but inside, the stairway cut across it from bottom to top, with the separate triangle of three steps to break the line. There was never on earth another such window. How many hours I spent in its light I cannot calculate, reading, writing verses, making secrets like the private alphabet I shared with Carol. But even she did not know where I was when I sat in that closet. Often I heard her calling me, even saw her pass under the window, knowing that she had no idea she was seen. In summer a mass of hollyhocks bloomed just outside, and a few reached the height of the glass and tapped now and then in a friendly way. Bumblebees visited them and made a great rumbling at the pane. Now and then there was a hummingbird with its probing beak and wings singing on the air.

When Mother called me I would sit and listen for a

while and then put my things carefully away and slip out into the front hall. When the coast was clear, I would dart through the front doorway and around the house, sometimes in one direction and sometimes in another, appearing as if I might have been anywhere but in the house itself.

That day, I sat and ate that pomegranate, or drank— for it is nearer to drinking than to eating, after all—the bright juice around the hard seeds. I made a pile of the seeds, very neat, as I had made piles of apple cores in that closet many times. I had almost finished the second half, having made the fine discovery that a whole section of seeds could be lifted out and that it looked like a bunch of tiny, tight-packed grapes, when I heard Carol calling.

"Look at this, this is how it is *inside*," I told her, coming on the run around the house. "Taste."

We sat on the steps of the kitchen porch, and she took one on her tongue tentatively, as a taster will sample wine. It was too strange for her. "You should take it to show at school," she said.

"There's a story about pomegranates in the Bible." I thought this might persuade her to respect or patience. Her father was the Bishop of our Ward of the Mormon Church and religion was all-important in her house. Because I loved her as I loved nobody else, I had made a habit of going wherever she went. There was Primary on Monday, Religion Class on Tuesday, Sunday School on Sunday. When we grew older we were Beehive Girls and went to Mutual Improvement Association every week, a fine thing to do because it was there we met the boy friends who took us home. Sacrament meetings on Sunday nights were meeting places for all young lovers in our town, going there one of the weekly "dates" for those going steady. This was smiled upon, for love—

young and old—is a habit Mormons never include among the sins of mankind.

When I was eight years old I went to the Manti Temple with Carol one bright summer day and was baptized by immersion and blessed a Member of the Church of Jesus Christ of Latter Day Saints. My mother—unlike her own—encouraged me, and made a pretty pair of white pajamas for me to be baptized in. I heard her say to Dad, "When in Rome, do as the Romans do. I've learned that from the way it was with me."

"Have you been to *Italy?*" I asked, fresh from world geography and its capitals.

"Shall we read?" I asked Carol that day the pomegranates came. Even though she listened only politely to the fairy stories I read to her, Carol always loved to hear chapters from books I was currently interested in. She preferred *Little Women* and *Little Men* to *Huckleberry Finn* and *Lorna Doone*. We went through the Pollyanna books together, I reading while she sewed. She did not particularly care about my collection of shells and never hovered over my starfish or the coil of seaweed Grandmother had sent in another box. But for my doll furniture she made tiny cushions and miniature doilies, and she kept dresses on my dolls. Which is why, perhaps, I never learned to sew.

"There's not time," she said. "Did you forget, today is Religion Class."

In Religion Class just then we were learning about the History of the Church. It was a bloody and exciting story, as bloody and exciting as the story of the early Christians who were fed to the lions. This seemed to make it as true as anything in the New Testament. Not only did Christ hang upon a cross and die for us and his religion, but so did Joseph Smith, the Prophet of God.

As a matter of fact, it was the same religion that both died for—we had the Restored Gospel, lost to men after Christ had died. He had died in a strange exotic land almost two thousand years before. Brother Joseph died in Carthage, Illinois, more recently. I thrilled to the brave story of the cross and pressed thorns to my forehead to see how terrible it had been. But a six-shooter was equally terrible—one was riddled with holes, through the chest, the head—and I had *seen* such guns in the Pioneer Museum. And I had seen many of them in action in the Friday afternoon matinees.

Yet what was a matinee compared to the real story of a real man? The Prophet's friends smuggled a six-shooter to him where he was shut up in Carthage Jail. But when the wicked men came in a painted, jeering mob, he was like a Lancelot with a toothpick.

I must have had a good teacher, for the scene was vivid to me. "His brother Hyrum was hit in the nose . . . three other bullets struck him . . . when the mob stormed the jail, Joseph Smith emptied his gun down the corridor as they came. But there were too many." It was made especially vivid to me by the fact that one of my friends was a granddaughter of John Taylor, who was one of the Prophet's companions in the jail. He was shot, too, but saved by a miracle. A bullet struck the watch in his pocket, not only saving his life but preserving the very moment of the attack that was to go down in history forever.

"God meant him to be a President of the Church," my teacher said.

Miracles were daily bread to us.

"Some of the people," the teacher said one day, "were apostates, and it is known that a number of them were in the mob that day. They painted their faces so they would not be recognized. Imagine—they had been friends of the Prophet, they had even been baptized! It is hard to believe that anybody who had the privilege of knowing the Prophet himself could ever do such a terrible thing."

I knew his death intimately, as if I myself had been there. I knew how, with his friends dying around him and his gun empty, he rushed to the window of the upstairs room where he had been imprisoned. Down below were a hundred bayonets, and faces painted hideously, like Indians. Shot in the back, he tried to leap out, but clung for a moment to the sill. And then he fell. I could hear his voice crying "O Lord, my God!" which was as wonderful a thing to say as "Father forgive them, for they know not what they do."

"As he lay on the ground, one of the mob raised a bowie knife and rushed forward to cut off his head—" I can hear it to this day—"but at that very moment the storm clouds in the sky parted and the setting sun made a line of light through the June evening. The mob broke up and fled in every direction. . . ."

Why had not God stepped in a little earlier? I wondered. But He had a Plan, and now and then martyrdoms were necessary, the teacher said.

Real American history, that, along with tales of covered wagons attacked by red Indians on the Great Plains and people fleeing from besieged forts in the later villages. My own grandfather had been a hero, after all. "It was not only Gentiles and Indians the Pioneers had to fight," my teacher said. "Sometimes our own people turned against their friends. Just as Judas turned against Christ, these people turned against the Saints. Sometimes they went over to the Gentiles who came to open the mines and start the railroads. Just for money, they turned against their friends. And against God's work. Through wicked ways they lost their Testimonies of the Gospel's Truth, and even turned against Brother Brigham Young himself." I knew about some of the terrible towns started by Apostates and Gentiles, especially the railroad town of Corinne, north of Great Salt Lake City. I knew about the Utah War, when the Government of the United States sent an army against the People of God. That was a grand story too. "They camped over the mountain, but our men held them up there the whole winter long. Nobody could come in The Valley through that canyon unless Governor Young wanted them."

Why should I not thrill to every tale? I was a Saint myself, baptized in the White Temple up on Temple Hill. I had been promised many blessings if I remained faithful. Carol and I often carried our lunches up Temple Hill and sat on the grass looking at the towers and battlements of that building like a castle. We knew what was inside. We had climbed, the day we were baptized, up one of the winding stairways to a tower and looked out together, all set apart as we were, over the valley. Some day, we said in whispers, we would be married in that Holy Place.

How long after the Day of the Pomegranates the next letter came from Grandmother I cannot remember. But I recall Mother reading it at the supper table. "How wonderful—listen—Grandma is coming for a visit!"

We were delighted, all of us. Now there would be walks and talks and singing. Maybe she would wade with us again. Now there would be somebody willing to go on a picnic to the mouth of the canyon. She always had time, as Mother never did. She had shown us how to make sandwiches the easiest way, buttering the end of the loaf to make the cool butter spread more easily, thickly, smoothly. She knew a thousand ways of making life better.

"I hope you received the package," she had written,

"and that you enjoyed the fruit. Now I'll be able to bring a good deal with me, with my baggage. There is a new law, did you hear about it, and I'll be able to get a pension finally for what your father did in the Blackhawk War. But I have to get some affidavits to put with my papers. I need to find three people who know what he did and who will fill out blanks for me. I should think Brother Jensen would be one, wouldn't you? And Brother Christensen, of course, though he's living in Moroni now, I think, with his daughter's family. I hope he's still alive. I'm forever hearing about old friends who die and it makes me feel terribly old. But surely three of them are left. Think of some, if you can, and inquire for me."

Then came the sentence that froze me in my chair. "Do you think they will be willing to do a favor like that for a wicked old apostate like me?"

I sat staring at my mother while she went on reading to the end. And then I said, "Mother—what was it she said about—about the *apostate?*" I must have heard it wrong. It had to be another word.

Mother handed me the letter. I could read it for myself. And there it was—"a wicked old apostate like me." Even the word "wicked." I looked up, with what wide eyes I can imagine, and saw that Mother and Dad were both watching me. "What is an apostate?" I asked. The teacher had been wrong, of course, and yet the word "wicked" was also there—

"Somebody who leaves a church," Mother said, matter-of-factly.

My face was hot but my hand, holding the letter, felt cold. "Do you mean—like the people who—" I couldn't even say it.

She understood and smiled at me. "In the early days they did some bad things, is that what you mean?" she asked. She looked at my father.

His face was serious and he leaned forward over his plate to speak to me. "Your grandmother didn't mean wicked like *that*," he said. "She meant it for some kind of joke in her letter. But she did leave the Church. She—" He paused. I could see it was rather difficult for them to explain.

Mother said gently, "Your grandmother had a very hard life here when she was young. Her mother was a second wife—you've seen your great-grandfather's grave with his three wives—and there were lots of children and hard times, sometimes not even enough to eat or to wear. Sometimes when there was trouble about polygamy, her father had to hide for weeks at a time." Her face looked anxious. And I honestly did not find these reasons enough. In the history I had learned, hardship was welcome, actually an incentive to more and more faith. Weren't the brave pioneers troubled with drought and crickets and floods as well as wild Indians? They had to dig sego lily roots for food. Why didn't Grandmother go out and dig sego lily roots? She herself had shown one to me, had peeled the white bulb. . . .

"Well, *say* it," Dad said to Mother. "She was a freethinker from the time she was a girl. She even demanded a *vote*, right along with Susy Young Gates and the rest of them." He began to laugh. "Quite a girl!" he said.

But I didn't laugh. I rose with dignity, feeling numb and confused. After the dishes were done, I went down cellar and looked at the rest of the pomegranates, keeping cool down there in the earth. I carried one up and asked Mother if I could have it. "Of course," she said. "I don't think the others like them much, anyway. I'm glad you do." And she raised her voice as I went out with it. "Your Grandma will be glad you do."

In the closet the sun was sending its last rays through the magic window. I sat holding the fruit in my hands as the window turned red and orange and yellow and then faded into evening and blackened into night. I could see Grandmother picking fruit from a bright tree in the morning. "Let us get up early to the vineyards. . . ." She was reading the Bible for poetry, she had said. When she came I would ask her about it. Each of us was responsible for our fellow man, my teacher had said so. Each of us was a missionary, whether we went on missions to foreign countries or stayed right at home. "We must teach by our own example," she had said, "by how we ourselves live."

As Carol and I had done for other wicked people, I bowed my head over the ripe fruit and prayed earnestly that my dear grandmother might see the light.

Nothing special remains in my memory about that particular visit, which seems odd now. If I preached to Grandmother, she mercifully made nothing much of it, and I probably prayed in secret. She did not stay long; she never did. "I come long enough to see that you are all right," she once said, "and then it is time for me to go. A family should never be forced to harbor an outsider for very long." She was the first to say, in my hearing, that a visitor was like a fish, stinking after the third day. I thought she had made it up herself. We had a splendid hike that visit, I remember, and a picnic by a mountain lake, the whole family. And I went with her on a short trip on a train to visit some old friends, up the valley. One day she waded with us when we persuaded her, holding her skirts to her knees and laughing and shuddering. "That's for youngsters," she said. "I had my turn at it."

She went to Sunday School with me the only Sunday she was there, and perhaps that was to comfort me. I remember being agonized by two boys in my class who behaved badly. Certainly *they* were not setting a good example. One of them took twelve pieces of bread from the sacrament plate and asked his friend how many *he* got, an incident I considered sufficiently important to report, outraged, in my diary. I can see myself, shocked righteously, my hands folded in my clean lap.

So Grandmother went away again and the years passed. I grew to love her letters and had a correspondence with her myself when I went off to school. She began to represent something entirely different to me. I was sad when she abandoned the lush fruits and flowers of California and went to Nevada to be near her eldest daughter. Somehow California had been right for her as the desert never seemed to be in spite of the special beauties she found there. "You must come at Eastertime," she wrote, "when the desert is in bloom. The most brilliant flowers in the world bloom here, all the more beautiful for all those thorns."

Why Mother took me with her to Grandmother's during her last illness, I still wonder. Mother needed strength just then and I had always been one to begin shivering and then burst into tears. Did she feel that *I* needed to learn strength, I wonder? Even in the last days of her life, writhing with pain and calling out, Grandmother was strong. In those long days in the presence of her death I thought constantly about her and about her life and asked Mother many questions. Grandmother had always come to us when we needed her, when the babies were born, when we had flu, when Dad and Mother took their once-in-a-lifetime trips to San Francisco and to New York. In every family crisis, she had been there. For years I had felt that from the sunset, which was named California, came rescue. She moved about the rooms and order entered, like sun through a window.

I looked at the treasures she had collected, many exactly like those she had sent to me. Special shells and stones, relics of the sea she had loved. Flowers, leaves, a sprig of sage from the mountains, still fragrant when it was crushed. One bit of special quartz I remembered seeing her pick up and put into her pocket one high blue day.

What a pocket! I thought, looking at Grandmother's intelligently selected clothes in a closet that smelled like a cedar chest. When we lost something and came wildly, crying, "Somebody took my best Easter egg!" or "Where is my doll? my book? my key?" she would look at us in disgust and say, "Why, *it's in my pocket*." At first we actually looked there, not understanding. But one day I came shouting, "Where are my roller skates? *Somebody—*" And when she said, laughing, that the wicked Somebody had put them in her pocket, I suddenly knew what she meant. Why was I so foolish? Why did I go around shouting instead of looking in all of the *possible* places?

That same pocket always yielded real things, like peppermints when one's mouth was just watering for peppermints.

Looking at her cluttered shelves and crowded drawers, I began to notice her books.

The very first day Mother sat down to read *Science and Health*. "Mother reads this a lot," she said, "but still she sends for the doctor and respects everything he says." She told me about her eleven brothers and sisters, few of whom I knew, since they had scattered out of Zion. None had been baptized as I had. Two had married Catholics and were converted and had become deeply religious. The others had remained indifferent, even the two who had remained among the Saints. "She was baptized and she was married in the Endowment House in Salt Lake," Mother said. "Father died when I was eleven, and she had to work terribly hard to take care of us. She was determined that I should go on to school after I graduated from the Eighth Grade, but I got a job, and then—" Then she had married, at sixteen, and before she was twenty there were three of us, I knew. "All the boys had to go to work early," she said. "Mose worked in the mines, in Eureka, and that's where he was hurt, later."

Eureka, I knew, was a Gentile town. It had bars and poolrooms.

For hours I looked at the books, while Grandmother cried out. They were full of marks and pressed flowers. One was by a man who wrote of Buddhism. "Sometimes," Grandmother had written in this book, "I wonder whether I am even a good Christian." How I should have seen her once, delivering the Good People to the lions! She had marked several fascinating passages. "Christians permit matrimony as a concession to weakness, but there is no real understanding of women. They are given souls, of course, and marriage protects them and their children as they were never protected by the Romans or the Greeks. But Christians love the souls of women, not their bodies, not how they are different from men but how they are the same."

Here she had written on a small slip of paper: "I recall the look of Mormon women. The portraits. Every one had those downward lips, the chastened anxious eyes. Cows. Polygamy did it. The Priesthood. They say Susy Gates always asked her little husband whether she could go out and give a lecture!" The exclamation point is hers.

She had marked Mills' "On Liberty" very deeply with a sharp pencil. The quote from Von Humboldt in support of individuality was ringed with ink. Individuality, he said, was "one of the elements of well being," and from a union of freedom and the variety of situations might arise "individual vigor and manifold diversity." She wrote in large letters beside this: "Good!"

One of the books I remembered her bringing along on a visit when I was in high school. It had seemed a book for children, then, and I recall how she read from it to my younger sister. Now I opened it, a large book with thick paper and many drawings and short sentences and paragraphs. Hendrick Van Loon's *The Story of the Bible*. It opened to a page that told about "The Song of Songs."

"The Song of Songs is in reality a very old love poem. . . . The heroine is a shepherdess. The King has seen her and has taken her away from her home in the village of Shunem. He has given her an honoured place in his harem. He tried to gain her favour. But she, the simple Shulamite, remains faithful to her shepherd lover. She has been installed in a lovely apartment in the heart of the royal palace. But she thinks only of the happy days when she and her own man wandered across the hills and tended their flocks. . . ."

Now Grandmother's respectful marks began. "The Song of Songs is not a religious book, but it is the first evidence of something new and very fine which had at last come into the world. In the beginning of time, woman had been a beast of burden. She belonged to the man who captured her. She worked his fields. She looked after his cattle. She bore his children. She cooked for him . . . and in return she received the morsels from his table. But all this is beginning to change. Woman is coming into her own. She is recognised as the equal of man. She is his companion. She inspires his love and she receives it. Upon this firm foundation of mutual respect and affection, a new world was soon to be built."

Then the swift script: "But we are no better than the Negroes, we have not got the Priesthood!"

I went to the door of her bedroom and looked at her. "Grandmother," I said.

But she was in too much pain for questions or for answers, and I returned to the books. She read detective stories, and I could imagine her on many lonely nights solving the problems. She had all of Conan Doyle in a red leather-bound set, one volume containing a marked "Study in Scarlet."

"Belief," she had marked once more in another book, "is not in itself an indication of truth. Though we have to act on faith, in the quest for truth faith is no substitute for evidence. Faith is nothing more than a state of satisfaction with received beliefs . . . nor is the comfort which an idea gives a mark of its truth. . . ."

She had admired Bertrand Russell, especially his ideas on education. He believed that "the teacher should love his children better than his State or his Church." She had written, and I trembled as I read it, remembering many things she had said and done when I was a child: "Children must be left to find their own way. It is not love if you try to mold them. . . . They should be loved for how they are different, for their independence, for thoughts of their own."

Mother sent me to the drugstore with a prescription and I was glad to go out of the house and walk. In the evening I walked to the edge of town into the desert and saw the sun go down. Yes, the desert was beautiful even when it was not in bloom. I was amazed at the abruptness of nightfall, and came home in the dark.

Mother was giving a bed bath and I heard her say, "But I can't wash you properly with those garments on. It's foolish to wear them in bed all the time. The doctor says—"

Grandmother's voice was pained, not her own. "No— leave them—leave them—"

I knew what they were talking about without going in to see. We had spoken of this at home when Grandmother came for a visit and her clothes were washed with ours. How odd she should go on wearing the undergarments of the Mormon Church, the white symbolic underwear with marks over the breasts, the navel, and the knee. In the beginning of the Church, the legs came to the ankle, the sleeves to the wrist, and they had been tied instead of buttoned. By the time I myself married in the temple and wore them, strategic revelations had permitted alterations in length of sleeve and leg that made them more acceptable under modern clothes. But the marks remained the same.

Mother said, "You don't believe in all that, Mother! You've said so ever since I can remember. So *why*—"

As I entered the room, Grandmother pulled herself onto her elbows. Her voice was strong from her frail body, ravaged with illness. "I made a promise, that's why," she said. "And when I make a promise, I keep it!"

In one's youth, there are promises. I knew. She told us in which drawer she kept her temple clothes, the white dress and veil and the green embroidered apron. Washed and pressed and ready, she said.

Ready to be worn in her coffin and her grave. And so they were; when the time came, very soon after that, Mother saw to it. The promise was kept.

"What shall we have read at her funeral?" Mother asked, pale with exhaustion and grief. "You decide—you know what she loved—"

It was easy to find in her Bible the passages she had loved the most. "Judge not and ye shall not be judged . . . forgive and ye shall be forgiven . . . bless them that curse you . . . for he maketh his sun to rise on the evil and on the good, and sendeth rain on the just and on the unjust . . . when thou prayest, thou shalt not be as the hypocrites are: for they love to pray standing in the synagogues and in the corners of the streets, that they may be seen of men. . . . But thou, when thou prayest, enter into thy closet, and when thou hast shut thy door, pray to thy Father, which is in secret. . . ."

Perhaps some thought it strange that there should be at the very end, "Let us get up early to the vineyards; let us see if the vine flourish, whether the tender grape appear, and the pomegranates bud forth. . . ."

First Love

It was just before my eleventh birthday that I saw Jiggs for the first time. That long ago! Yet, even now, if I suddenly see a blaze of eyes along a highway, or if I hear cats consorting in the alley down the block at night, the feeling comes again. Still strong, as if it were a clue.

He was no particular kind of cat. His mother was Hansen's Tabby, a beautiful animal, but who could know who his father was? Ralph Hansen insisted it was Old Yellow Eyes, and from what happened, I'm inclined to believe that he was right. Yellow Eyes was a wildcat, as we called the homeless creatures who ranged in the barns and orchards and woodpiles of the town. They were supposed to be able to "live off the land," hunting. But they were uncommonly fond of milk, enough to battle for it, as if they all remembered gentler days.

That year we had our milk from Hansen's, four quarts a day. Claude and Helen and I took turns going after it. I liked to go, especially when I could be early enough to watch Ralph Hansen milk. He was a big, freckled boy, ugly and loud like his father, and a great tease. Mother liked our milk to be "strained," and I never told her how often Ralph filled our buckets directly from the cows. He would turn a teat up and make an arc of milk that barely missed me. "Supper's ready," he would say. "Catch it!"

It was fun to try. But that wasn't what I really enjoyed about the milking. The good part was the coming of the cats.

There were at least a dozen ranging that neighborhood. Ralph had collected bits of old glass and crockery that he set out in a long row before he began to milk. Soon, as he worked, there would be a streak of motion in one direction, and then in another. Eyes stared down from the rafters. Around the stacked hay in the loft, something black crept. It was exciting, magic. I would hear one leap over my head, another would appear in the barn door. Big and little, every variation of cat color, they came for their supper. Every eye was on Ralph as the milk hissed into the buckets.

At last he would turn and pick up a dish. Then the stir really began, a tense creeping, closer, closer. He filled each dish to the brim; they always had high foamy heads on them, like beer. If a cat came too close before he was finished, Ralph would suddenly hiss it away. At last he turned, grinning, and let them come and get it.

I don't know how the rules had been made, but rules there were. "One cat for each dish" was the most important one. It was a scramble like musical chairs. If two cats arrived at one dish they would turn on each other with an awful howl, snarling and spitting. It was terrible and wonderful to watch. Ralph loved it, I'm sure, and loved causing it.

As for me, I liked it and hated it at the same time, the way I always felt at a scary movie.

Sometimes, while one pair were fighting another cat would take over their dish, and then the two would turn on the newcomer. As soon as he went off to lick his wounds, they went back to their own fight until it was settled.

"Why don't you ever have enough dishes for them all?" I asked one night. "You do it this way on purpose, just for the fights."

But he shook his head. "How many cats can we afford to feed around here?" he asked, in disgust. "Ma says eight's the limit and that's a quart a day. She says we should stop feeding them entirely. But they come all the time. . . ."

The Hansens seemed to attract stray dogs too. They fed everything. Brother Hansen told a story on himself about the squirrels on the place. If they carried off all his nuts he bought a sack and put it out around Christmas.

"Ma says one more cat'll drive her out of her mind," Ralph said. "Sometimes they get to howling at night and you'd think we lived in a jungle."

That was true. I had heard them myself, shivering, when I had to walk that street in the dark.

Both Ralph and I liked Yellow Eyes the best. He was the biggest and he never failed to get his dish. A lot of the other cats had ripped ears and raggedy coats, but he was sleek and fine and seldom had to fight. He just walked in and took what he wanted and that was that. Sometimes a stranger came in and had to learn who he was. But only once. He was yellow all over, eyes and fur, striped as if he had tiger in his blood.

That particular night was Friday and I was too late for the milking because I had been to the matinee. It had been an especially long show because there were two serials besides the feature and the comedy. Those serials gave us no rest, and of course they were what we always went for. How could you stay away when the hero and heroine were tied to a railroad track with an engine coming, or hurtling down from crumbling bridges, or lifting cups of unsuspected poison to their lips? When one serial finally ended with everybody but the mean people safe and sound, the first chapter of the new one followed without delay.

Mother was cross, I remember. She had used up all her milk in custard and needed more for supper. "Don't you hang around there tonight. You come *directly* back," she called after me.

Hansen's kitchen was almost as much fun as the barn. I arrived that night just as they were sitting down to supper. Sometimes, when they had company or when they had extra help for planting or harvesting, I've seen as many as twenty at that table. There were always animals, too, and a noisy cage of canaries.

Sister Hansen was a strong, thick woman who did everything in a huge way. Chicken came to her table heaped on platters, potatoes in snowdrifty piles with pools of fresh butter in the middle. In summer she always had an immense bowl of lettuce from the garden, over which cream was poured in thick lumps and sugar sprinkled. She seemed always to be baking bread in a range that filled one wall. Her cakes were vast and untidy, frosted with gusto in brilliant pinks and unlikely greens. She never seemed to get the frosting thick enough, for it encircled the bottom of every cake like a thick moat and hung in dripping loops around the edges.

Yet the cake beneath was invariably delicious. Sister Hansen said she had two cakes in her life, a dark and a light. Who needed more? Devil and angel. Winter and summer. Devil's food was winter, black with chocolate and thick with nuts. In the spring, when the chickens were laying well, she returned to angel food, using dozens of eggs.

It was good to come out of the dusk into that warm and lively room. One lingered in the fragrant plenty until the cake appeared.

That night Ralph looked at me and winked. "You missed a good fight tonight," he said. "Old Yellow Eyes mopped up on a gray one and a white one together."

"There was a good matinee," I said, to make up for having missed the cats. "There's a new serial about Chinatown."

"Anyway, you can see the kittens," Molly, the littlest Hansen, said importantly. "They're in the wood box." She wriggled out of her chair, and at once her sister must help with the show. The wood box, with a bit of blanket in it, had been set in a nice warm place behind the big stove. Inside was the one tame cat on the place, a lovely tabby, sleek and fat like her mistress. She lay with dreamy eyes, contented, and climbing blindly around her in an endless search for dinner were six of the most beautiful little animals I had ever seen.

Every single one was a ball of gold the color of Yellow Eyes. I knelt beside the box, enchanted. Comical and sprawling, they searched the world with their prickly paws and their nuzzling chins. Perfect ears, whiskers already. They made a marvelous tiny mewing.

Molly seized one by the scruff of its neck. "Tab doesn't care if we hold them," she said proudly. "She *likes* us to hold them."

"She doesn't either," her sister said. "She worries. Look at her." But she took one too.

"They were born outside and she brought every one of them in, right up to the door," Molly said. "She had them in her mouth, by their necks, but not one was hurt." She held the kitten in the circle of her fingers and it made a little howl.

"You're hurting it," I said.

"I'm not. That's just the way Tab does it."

Sister Hansen came in from the milk room with my two full buckets. "Tab's always been a good mother," she said in her indulgent voice. "Whichever one of those wildcats is their father, she doesn't trust him with her kits. She always fetches them in to us right away."

Ralph suddenly laughed. "It's old Yellow Eyes this time. I know *that*," he said.

The kitten in Molly's hands mewed unhappily, and Tab came anxiously to investigate, rubbing close.

"You two come finish your supper," Sister Hansen said, "and let the kittens finish theirs." And to me, "How about some cake?"

I explained I had to hurry, but when Molly said, "They've just got their eyes open. Feel how *little*—" and laid the kitten in my hands, I sat still. I not only felt how little, I felt how fragile, how bony-furry, how soft. How golden and helpless. And it looked up at me, and I felt how comical with its wrinkled nose. Its claws were like pins barely pricking, lovely. When I lifted it to my cheek, the fur was incredibly soft, like a baby's skin.

"That's the one with funny eyes," Molly said from the table.

I believe it was at that moment I knew this kitten belonged to me. Because when I looked at its eyes it looked directly back. My heart seemed to turn over. One eye was green, the other blue.

"You like cats so much," Ralph said, "why don't you take one along? Ma says we've got to give them all away."

"Or drown them," Molly said.

"It was your father said *that*," Sister Hansen said, giving her a warning mother-look that I knew very well. "Of course you're welcome to take any one you want," she said to me. "Take your pick. They're good cats. There's no better mouser than Tab, she's the best we ever had."

There were wonderful yellow flecks in the kitten's eyes, like the lines in a marble. Its ears were like shells.

But I was remembering something. "My mother won't have cats around," I said. "She likes birds in our yard."

"Cats don't hunt birds if you give them plenty to eat," Ralph said. "We have plenty of birds in *our* yard, and if anybody ever had more cats—"

Sister Hansen looked proudly at her canaries. "Tab's never paid any attention to birds. She's a mouser. She keeps our house and granary clear of mice the year around."

"Would you rather have a male or a female?" Ralph asked, as if it were settled. "There's three each."

Brother Hansen laughed. "Tab divides her litters, like we do," he said, and gave Sister Hansen a cheerful slap where she was the fattest. He had a huge laugh that sounded rich, as if he had just swallowed a mouthful of butter. He was so big that my brother once bet me a dime he had to have two chairs at the table.

"What is this one?" I asked.

Ralph came over, looking smart the way boys do when they know something girls don't. "That's male," he said.

But I knew it wouldn't make any difference to Mother, even though a female would be the worse of the two. I had heard her say that cats began having babies almost as soon as rabbits. "And you can't eat kittens," she had said.

What a terrible thing for her to say! I remembered it in despair, gazing down at the golden creature in my hands. It looked up at me with its strange eyes and made a sound, the smallest mew I ever heard. On my lap it began to search about, kneading and sprawling. Its motions and its warmth gave me a lovely feeling. Tab watched, anxiously, and moved back and forth between her box and this missing child.

"Here, I'll put him back for you, Tab." I gathered the kitten up tenderly and returned him to his brothers and sisters. But I knew him from the others already, even without looking at his eyes. He was the yellowest. He had special rings at the tip of his tail and the final one was perfectly white.

The telephone rang.

"Oh, dear, that's Mother!" I picked up my buckets and started for the door, while Molly and her sister rushed to answer, arguing on the way: "It's my turn!" "It isn't!"

"I'll ask her about the kitten," Sister Hansen said, and I stood still at the door, suddenly filled with hope. But it was not Mother; it was for Brother Hansen, who sighed and heaved himself out of his chair.

"We'll keep that one for you, just in case," he said kindly. "You just let us know. They shouldn't be moved for two weeks, anyway."

As I closed the door behind me, he was talking loudly on the telephone. But I thought only of the last words he said to me. *Two weeks.*

Maybe, in that much time, I could make Mother understand. Two weeks. Already, it seemed all the time I had to live.

I began to run, but the milk splashed up in the buckets and out from under the lids. Mother would be cross enough already, me being so late. I'd better not mention anything about cats tonight. And tomorrow—I would do everything right. I would clean up my room. Straighten my drawers. I would empty all the wastepaper baskets. I would dry the dishes—maybe even wash them —without being told. Even if it wasn't my turn. Maybe I'd better tell Carol not to call me up at the usual time.

We had an arrangement to call each other so we wouldn't have to help clear up after supper.

Two weeks. I stopped running, holding the buckets carefully on either side, but my heart was pounding. Mother was always saying, "If you don't stop getting so excited about things, you'll make yourself sick." As I came to our house, I saw her waiting on the porch. "Where on earth have you been all this time?" she asked. "Watching those awful cats?"

My face seemed to burst into flame. Sometimes I had an awful conviction that my mother could read my mind. "No, Ralph was through milking," I said.

The whole family waited with empty glasses. While Mother filled them I washed my hands and slipped into my place. But my heart still beat hard. There was a strange lump in my throat. I sat fiddling with my food and thought of the kitten.

"You're quiet tonight," Dad said, smiling at me. "Cat got your tongue?"

Once more my face went hot in a great wave. Why should he say that tonight? "No. I was just thinking," I said.

"Thinking!" My brother laughed. It is odd how brothers will have an idea their sisters can't think. I didn't answer or even so much as give him a glance. All I wanted to do now was get away from that table and go to my room and be alone.

Mother looked at me suspiciously. "You must have eaten some of that rich cake over there," she said.

I shook my head. Suddenly I wanted to cry. "I'm just not hungry," I said, and at that moment the telephone rang.

"Carol!" Helen said knowingly. "Mother, they do it on purpose—"

Another time I would have protested my innocence,

but somehow I couldn't. I went to the telephone, and it was Carol, all right, but I told her I couldn't talk to her that night, and it was true. "Tomorrow I'll tell you a secret," I said.

When I came back to the table, Mother looked sharply at me. "Do you have a fever again?" she asked. "You don't look right to me."

That was all I needed. When you feel sick only a little sympathy will make you cry. For several winters I had been rather a crybaby, I'm afraid, because I kept having bouts of tonsillitis. The doctor would make a date to take my tonsils out and then I would catch cold and it would be postponed. Sometimes I had earache too, and Mother would put warm cotton tabs, wet with paregoric, in my ears when I went to bed, and I wore an old velvet bonnet. It comforted me to feel my ears so warm and soon the medicine took the pain away, and I enjoyed a most luxurious sleep.

"If that child has tonsillitis *again!*" Mother said, getting up and heading for the medicine chest. "You lie down and I'll get the thermometer."

Helen said, "She's just pretending so she won't have to do the dishes." I've never in my life known anybody to hate dishes the way she did. And I can't blame her for being a bit jealous of all the time I spent in bed getting Mother's full attention. Being sick, unless I was in actual pain, was always pleasant because of the special things Mother did. The doctor was nice, too, an old family friend who let me listen with his stethoscope and look at the things in his bag. Sometimes, while he gossiped with Mother and Dad, I counted the pills in his bottles, and straightened out the swabbing sticks, and tucked the cotton neatly in its box. I liked having everybody stand around talking about me, and nothing made me feel more important than having a high temperature.

Now Mother looked at Helen and said, "It isn't possible to pretend about a temperature. If she doesn't have one, she can help you. If she does, she goes right to bed."

I went right to bed. Mother was so alarmed that she helped me undress and called for the doctor to come at once. I heard her say to Dad, "I hoped it wouldn't happen any more this winter. If we could just get them out and have it over with."

The doctor came and gave me pills and painted my throat. I hated the gagging, but I got the swabbing sticks afterward, and soon I was warm and cozy and heard the dishes being put away downstairs and the distant murmuring of the family. Then Mother came tiptoeing back, Dad following. I kept my eyes closed so I could hear what they said without their knowing I heard. I had learned how to make them think I was asleep when I wasn't. I would drop my mouth open a little and breathe very deeply and regularly, just now and then making a good snore. Nobody expects anybody to pretend he is snoring.

"I hope she'll be better before her birthday," Mother said.

"Sure she will. That's two weeks off." Dad was leaning over me, I could tell, and I was suddenly filled with gladness. My birthday. Two weeks. When they had gone I said my prayers again, especially thanking the good Lord for giving me tonsillitis again in the nick of time. Now I knew what I could do. . . .

That was the last time for several days that I had sense enough to say any prayers. The doctor came twice a day, and I had never been as sick as that before. They put a little white tent over my bed and Mother kept a steaming pot inside. It smelled nice, and never since have I smelled eucalyptus without remembering that tent over

me night and day, and my peculiar dreams. I made odd
noises and whistles when I tried to breathe, and there
seemed a great weight on my chest. I had pneumonia
as well as tonsillitis, and for over a week it was too painful
for pride. But then I began to get better.

Mother brought beautiful trays with miniature bou-
quets of geranium she clipped from the pots in her
kitchen windows. She used the prettiest napkins and her
nicest dishes. Carol came to see me and brought my
schoolbooks and a letter written by the whole class. Even
the teacher had put a note on it. I had never felt more
important in my life.

I was well enough, too, for making plans.

Mother brought my dolls, and a trunk of their clothes,
and the little bed the newest one slept in. If I had a
kitten, I thought, I would have it sleep in that bed instead
of a silly doll. Dolls didn't sleep anyhow; they were just
as well shut up in a box.

This doll was a very fine one I had got for Christmas,
only a little over a month before. She looked rather messy
and rumpled already, and Mother helped me fix her up.
I always pretended to like dolls because my sisters did
and so did Carol. I kissed her and undressed her and put
her pajamas on each night. But she was too beautiful
entirely; I didn't believe in her at all. There was nothing
about her to *watch*. She just lay there, like somebody in
a coffin. When I sat her up, of course, her eyes came
open with a click, but whenever she lay down she looked
absolutely dead. She had nice little ears, but they did not
twitch. She had pretty hands and neat painted nails, but
she could never scratch or reach. Her face was cold. She
made only one sound, a monotonous whining little "Ma-
ma" that came out of a box set into her back.

Animals are real, like people, I thought. Every single one
is different. Especially that one. Surely there was not an-

other kitten in the whole world with eyes like that. At first you might think those six kittens were all alike, but in half a minute you saw how different they were. I thought about Tab, such a handsome, sleek, and lazy cat. I thought of Yellow Eyes, fighting for his milk. How odd and wonderful it was for two such different cats as tame Tab and wild Yellow Eyes to have a family together!

Perhaps that was the reason for those strange and different eyes.

The first day I was really sitting up, Mother sat beside my bed, talking and sewing and having a cup of tea. This was especially cozy, for she gave me a little in hot milk, with a cooky to soak in it. The sun was shining in the window, I remember, and Mother said contentedly, "What a beautiful day for February. And now you're going to be well enough to eat some of your birthday cake. For a while you had us worried."

I cleared my throat, which was still a little sore. But before I could speak, she glanced at me and asked, "Have you decided what you want this year?"

My heart began to beat, hard and fast. Now was the moment. "Yes, I have," I said.

"Good! What is it?"

For a second I closed my eyes and *wished*. Then, in a small voice I deliberately made sound sad and thick as if it still came from a very sore throat, I said, "It's something you maybe won't let me have. . . ."

She looked at me in surprise. "It is? What on earth wouldn't I let you have, for heaven's sakes?"

I swallowed, and it was true that this swallow came very hard. I was trembling. "It's—well, it's a kitten," I said.

"Oh—oh, I see." She had stopped sewing and sat looking at me. "It's not that I don't like cats, really," she said at last. "You know that. Don't you remember that awful cat our neighbors had and those bluebird feathers we found on the porch all the time—"

For that I was ready. "Ralph Hansen says cats never eat birds if there are plenty of mice to eat. And if you give them lots of milk."

She began to sew again and I held my breath. Then I said, raptly, "Mother, these kittens are the most beautiful ones I ever saw. You know Tab, Sister Hansen's big cat. They're hers. That's why I was late that night I got sick— they were in the wood box and I held one. He's—" It was hard to tell her how wonderful he was. I tried to describe him, but it was useless except for his color and the odd thing about his eyes. It was like trying to describe the waves of the sea, or flames in a fire. "He sort of sticks, like a little round burr. And he's so soft—he's the *soft-est—*"

"Do you have to have the one with funny eyes?" she asked. "I always feel I'd rather have *normal* things."

"He's the one I want," I said firmly. Perhaps even passionately, for he had been the only one from the first moment. "It doesn't seem funny about his eyes—not really. You hardly notice at first. And then it's just—" I was helpless again. It was just him, part of *him*. The way he was.

"Well, then," she said, looking resigned and yet loving, as if my request had actually pleased her, "if that's what you want, of course you must have it. People should always get what they want for their birthdays." She frowned at me. "But you'll have to promise to take good care of it. A cat is not a doll."

That I knew very well. "Oh, I will—I promise I will!" I cried.

"I'll call Sister Hansen tonight and see about it," she said.

I lay back on my pillow, weak with excitement. "I don't want anything else, Mother, not another thing," I said.

"Maybe a kitten will be a good thing for you," Mother smiled at me. "It might help keep you quiet a while. The big trouble with you, the doctor says, is that you get up and run too soon, every time. This time you've got to stay right in that bed a solid month and then get those tonsils out."

I didn't care now. I would have company all the time, every day. "A little responsibility won't hurt you, either," she said. "It's good to learn to take good care of a living thing."

When Dad came home, she went to meet him, as always. Soon he came in to see how I was. "So you're feeling better today. That's good—it'd be too bad to have a birthday and not be able to eat a scrap of your own cake and ice cream."

Before I could tell him about the kitten, he asked: "Do you know what you want yet?"

"Yes. Yes, I *do!*" I savored the telling, the prelude of possession. "May I have anything I want? *Anything?*"

"Well—" He laughed in his wonderful teasing way. "Anything in reason. I'm not a millionaire. If you should want a mink coat, now, or a diamond necklace or something like that—"

"What I want doesn't cost anything," I said.

He shook his head. "I don't believe it. Everything in this world costs something, you might as well learn that first as last. Even Santa Claus sends a bill, the old miser, did you know that? There just *ain't any such animal as something that doesn't cost anything.*"

How odd and wonderful that he should say that, just then. "It *is* an animal," I cried in triumph.

From his laugh, I knew he had known about the kitten already, that Mother had told him.

"I told your mother it was all right with me," he said. "She's going to call up Sister Hansen right now. Did you choose the one you wanted?"

"Sister Hansen will know the one," I said.

From the couch where I lay during the day I could hear Mother at the telephone. When she came in and began to look up Hansen's number, I could hardly breathe. She looked at me and said, "You settle down, see? This kitten is supposed to calm you down, not get you all upset."

"I won't get upset. I *promise*." But I felt my heart going as she gave the number and waited.

"Hello. Hansen's? Is your mother there?"

She stood waiting. I could hear Sister Hansen's big voice when it came.

"I'm calling about that kitten my little girl wanted. . . . Yes, yes, I know, but it seems to be the one she wants. It's for her birthday. Friday. Yes. I'll see that she takes good care of it."

Sister Hansen talked and talked. I could hear what she said, a little, and knew she talked about Tab and what a good mouser she was and how good all of her kittens were.

Then Mother, "Yes, thanks, she's much better. But she won't be up for a while. . . . We think she'll be able to study at home and not get too far behind. I thought a kitten might help keep her quiet for a few weeks. She's so *active.* . . . Yes, I think so, too. Then, when their own children come along. . . ." She laughed at something Sister Hansen said.

Dad looked at me and winked. Sister Hansen was talking about the birds and we could hear her canaries singing; their cage was right next to her telephone.

"You think Friday will be all right, then. Thanks so much. Oh, that's good of Ralph, but I'm sure my son— Yes—well, if he really wants to, of course. Yes. Thanks again. Goodby."

She turned from the telephone. "Ralph will bring it over after school, Friday," she said. "You'll have it for birthday eve. And maybe then you won't feel so sorry for yourself, missing the matinee."

I laughed. Who cared about a silly thing like a matinee? She leaned down and gave me a quick kiss. I had never loved her so much. She didn't like cats, but she was going to let me have one anyway. That's how she was.

"Sister Hansen said if you didn't take good care of it, I was to send it right back," she said. "You know, you have a way of getting tired of things."

"Not of a *kitten!*"

"It must have a nice scratching box and you must keep it clean, see, with fresh sand every single day. We'll get a pretty dish and you must keep it absolutely clean. And you must never forget to feed this kitten—I don't want it to start thinking about birds. *Not one bird*—"

"Not one," I promised.

When my sisters came home, I told them. "I know it," Helen said, as always. She knew everything every time, whether she really did or not. But my little sister, Gerry, said in glad excitement, "I'll help you give it milk."

"No. Nobody must ever feed it but me. It must know it's *mine*," I said, and knew as I spoke how very important this was. Mine. *Mine.*

Friday seemed forever away. When it actually arrived, afternoon was forever away. Thank goodness, Ralph did not go to the matinees; he should be there soon after four o'clock. What if he had to do the milking first? The thought filled me with dismay.

When the paper arrived, just before four, I tried to get interested in the funnies. One of my favorite strips was about Maggie and Jiggs. That day it was especially good, it seemed to me, poor dear little Jiggs trying to sneak some corned beef and cabbage into stuck-up Maggie's grand house.

"What are you going to name that kitten?" Mother asked, coming in for a minute while I read. And I said suddenly, as if I had thought about it for a long time: "Jiggs. His name is Jiggs!" As I said it, like magic, somebody knocked on the back door.

I held my breath. Mother opened the door and I heard her say, "Oh, he's cunning," and they came in.

Jiggs had grown incredibly since I had seen him. He was furrier than ever, prettier, and he did not sprawl and seek any longer. He already had a mind of his own. At once he began to wriggle to free himself from Ralph, from me, to get on with exploring the great hills and valleys of my bed.

I have forgotten everything about those next few weeks except the enchantment of my new companionship with Jiggs. Holding him. Being forever charmed by his kittenness which could seem suddenly tender, even wise. Soon after he came I had my tonsils out, but I remember nothing about the operation, only how wonderful it was to return home to Jiggs and the bed again.

He was never twice exactly the same. He loved to bunch the covers, apparently pretending they were other kittens. He would turn his back on them elaborately and walk away, then suddenly turn, as if to surprise them, and *pounce*. He would turn so quickly sometimes that he threw himself into a somersault. He would follow a string I pulled, pouncing and playing and making a great fuss, finally capturing it triumphantly. He loved searching for a small red ball I hid among the pillows. Or for a little bell I tinkled, first here and then there. Or for the tips of my toes when I slipped them in and out of the covers to tease him.

Sometimes it was enough just to watch him at his own

living. His washing was the prettiest and most delicate operation in the world and I never tired of it. His mother had taught him a great deal in that little time. But then, of course, he was a *very* bright child.

And eating. Beautiful! His tongue was like a tiny red flag, flicking in and out of the white milk. Incredible, the jolly fuss over a bit of salmon.

Soon he would come flying when I called. "Jiggs! Jiggs! Kitty-kitty-kitty!" He loved me as I loved him. I knew it.

In two weeks I was well enough to return to school, and I was glad enough to see my friends and my teacher. I loved school always. It was fine to ride a bicycle again, to feel well, to breathe deep and run hard, not to get tired or to cough or to sniffle. Yet the happiest part of every day was when I arrived home and Jiggs rushed to greet me. Mother told everybody that he could tell time. "At four o'clock he sits by the door and waits," she said.

He also knew when it was time to wake me in the morning. It was enchanting to wake to his little mewings and pouncings and cuddlings. Sometimes he came right up and patted my face; it is true. And one of the things he taught me to do that I have been doing ever since is to wake properly and enter the world each day with a new pleasure. I noticed he never woke from a nap suddenly and never jumped right up. He would open one eye, then the other, close them both again, squinting, and try once more whether the light was right. He would stretch a leg, another leg, and then stretch his back and curl himself up, and then uncurl himself. He moved link by link, as it were, all over, getting into the way of motion once again. I began to try it myself, and am convinced that the only good way to waken oneself is bit by bit.

In a few weeks he began to be entirely cat, not kitten. He became sleek and beautiful and walked with dignity.

Washing was a very serious matter. Only now and then he played in the old way, and I felt he was pretending to be a kitten again for my pleasure.

Summer came, and there was another world of grass and trees and flower beds. He walked among the small new plants with lovely, careful cushion-feet. His tail would curl around the stalks, but gently. He played with blossoms and watched bumblebees and pretended to stalk a butterfly.

His sound was one of the best things about him, winter and summer. Like a teakettle on the boil, sometimes. Or like a dove in the early morning. He would lie in my lap, by the fire or, later, in the sun, and as I stroked him he would begin his murmuring, and it would grow into a huge humming deep inside that vibrated clear to his claws and trembled in my fingers.

The birds went right on singing in our trees.

Summer ended and school began again. It was that fall, when Jiggs was about eight months old, that the troubled time began. It was nobody's fault, actually, I can see that now. But it was hard for me to see it then.

Salt Lake City was Utah's biggest city, and I thought it must be the biggest in all the world. Several times a year we went there to visit my father's mother over a week end. Once I thought of taking Jiggs along, but he hated going in the car and tried desperately to leap from the window. So he was left that October day, and Carol promised to visit him and feed him.

I would have hated going away, except that I loved the excitement of the city. It was wonderful, for a country child, to see the houses thicken and the buildings rise up and hear the noises begin. My grandmother lived on State Street and one could see the dome of the capitol from her front porch. Not far from her place was a park with a merry-go-round and a little lake with boats and lovely flower beds.

Besides everything else, my grandmother had a wonderful dog that we all loved. She called him Deecher, after a famous outlaw, she said, and he needed a strong name. He was huge and brown, a police dog so handsome that whenever we took him walking people stopped to look at him. His little yard behind Grandmother's house was so small that he was always wild to get out of it, and pulled so hard on the leash we had to take turns holding him. Only on one of the huge lawns at the park could we let him go free for a while, and it was there we always played the Game.

It was done with an old broomstick and a gunny sack. Claude ran as fast as he could, holding the sack high in the air on the end of the stick. Deecher would run after him and all of a sudden he would leap, trying to pull the sack down. He could leap beautifully. The fun was in teasing him, keeping the sack just out of reach, so that he had to leap higher and higher. People always stood about watching and laughing. Finally he would get the sack and everybody clapped and cheered for him. Then he would protect it, holding it in his teeth while we all tugged to get it away. Growling and shaking his head, he pretended to be very fierce with us. Finally he let us win and stood, alert and eager, for the first part of the Game once more.

When we arrived he was in the yard, running back and forth like a tiger in a cage. This was always the same, and we could hardly wait to take him out, just as he could hardly wait to be taken. But Grandmother said he could not go with us any more. "I've had to get a chain to keep him from jumping the fence," she said. "It's fastened to the clothesline so he can run a little."

Claude was shocked. "A *chain?*"

"He started to run away, and he chased trucks. They told me they'd impound him the next time."

"What's impound?" I asked.

And Claude said grimly, "It's to lock him up. A pound is an animal jail."

All evening Grandmother had to speak to him every now and then about barking. Early the next morning, I heard her scolding him out of the back window. Claude said, "He can't even *bark!*"

That day it was not fun in the park even though it was a beautiful day. Claude said, "Dogs have a good, free life in a little town," and we knew what he meant. We had big lawns and gardens and wide, free streets and plenty of vacant lots. Dogs trotted off to visit each other, just the way people did, and they helped herd cows and sheep and ran alongside horses and were included in family picnics in the mountains and even rode on lakes with fishermen in their little boats. We had a place called a Stray Pen in our town, but it was not like a jail, it was only a place to keep animals safe when they were lost, a place where they could be fed and watered until their owners came for them.

It was not surprising, when we were ready to leave, that Grandmother said, "I wish you could take Deech along with you. He's so miserable now. I thought he must be sick and took him to the vet. But there's nothing really wrong with him, except his own energy. He pulls so I simply can't walk him any more."

Claude cried, "Dad, could we? Mother—"

"I've never thought of having such a *big* dog," Mother said.

Just as I had promised about Jiggs, Claude said passionately, "I'll take care of him myself. *Honest.* We'll get a kennel—"

I was actually on his side, something I found it hard to

believe afterward. Deecher would be a show dog, the only police dog in our town. He could play the Game on our own lawn; it was plenty big enough.

"He's an outdoor dog," Grandmother said. "If I had realized, I'd never have had him here. I thought a watch-dog in a city—" She looked at me with a smile. "He gets along fine with cats," she said. "He never pays the least attention to the ones in the alley."

"Well—" Mother said.

Deecher loved the car. It was nice to have him on the floor and to sit with our feet warm in his fur. He seemed to like it, and we rubbed him and patted him. We left Grandmother's about sundown and soon, as always on that long trip, we stopped our chatter and fell asleep. In no time, Dad was saying, "Here we are!"

While I struggled blindly with my shoes, thinking of Jiggs waiting in the house, I heard Mother say, "Until he gets used to things, I suppose he'd better sleep in the kitchen—" I heard nothing more, for I was on my way and at that moment Deecher meant nothing to me.

Jiggs was waiting by the door. I didn't even have to call his name. As I took off my coat and hat he made his long warm twistings around my ankles, as always, telling me all the news. And then, suddenly, he stiffened. He made a sound I had never heard from him before—*ppppfffftttt!*—like that. And then he vanished.

When I finally got him out from under the couch and quiet on my lap, in my own room, I told him about poor Deecher. "You'll soon be good friends," I said. "Soon he'll stay outdoors in his own little house, anyway. But it would be nice if you could eat together. . . ." I had actually seen a dog and a cat eating from the same dish, at the Hansens'.

But the moment I let him off my lap he was under my bed. He refused to come to his own little bed at all, that night, and woke me long before dawn, pacing and mewing. Something alien was in the house now, and he could find no rest.

That first day, when I came home from school, he was not waiting at the door. Mother said he had not come out of my room the whole day long. "Deecher's been barking," she said. "Dad thought he should be tied until he feels at home. But I don't know—" She looked out of the window. Deecher had a longer run on our clothesline, but he wanted to be free, of course. "He feels strange here," she said. "Poor fellow."

I actually felt sorry for him too.

But when I went upstairs to find Jiggs, I was only angry at him. I had never seen Jiggs frightened or unhappy before. He lay under my bed and refused to come out at all. When I lay down I could see him, way back in the corner. His eyes looked big and round. They had never seemed so brilliant. I crawled under the bed to get close to him.

"Jiggs, you old silly, nobody is going to hurt you. I won't let anybody hurt you, don't you know that? Deecher is a nice dog—anyway, he'll be nice again when he stops barking. You'll be friends." I told him about the dog and cat at Hansens', and said, "Soon you and Deecher will eat from the same dish, too."

But for the time being, I promised him tenderly, he could eat right where he was. I crawled out and went downstairs and got his dish and filled it with warm milk. Then I brought it and set it under the bed, close to him.

For a long time he only lay still, trembling. But finally he moved to the dish and began to eat. He put his tongue out tentatively at first, and stood with it just in the milk, listening. Deecher was quiet for the time being, and Jiggs began to eat just as he always did, his tongue flicking fast in and out of the dish. But suddenly Deecher barked, and Jiggs leaped back so suddenly that the bowl upset and milk went running into the rug. Far back in the corner, Jiggs crouched and shivered.

I was cross about the milk. Now I had to clean it up, and I knew Mother wouldn't like it that the rug would be spotted and sour-smelling. I found a damp sponge and cleaned the place as well as I could with my head practically stuck in the springs above.

"See what you did," I said to Jiggs. "Just for being so *silly—*" I tried to get him to come out again when I had finished, but he wouldn't stir. Then I made a bad mistake. I became impatient with him and crawled under the bed again and took hold of him and dragged him out by the scruff of the neck. How terrified he looked! His mouth was drawn back over his teeth, and his eyes were like an owl's.

"Jiggs, *please!*" I was shocked that he should look at me as if I were an enemy.

He was tight all over. His tail was stiff and his fur stood out as if he were full of electricity. He tried to get away when Deecher barked again, struggling to get out of my lap and run back under the bed. But I held him, hard, trying to force him to lie down as he always did before. I began to stroke him and talk to him. But it was not until Deecher stopped barking at last that he softened at all. I stroked and stroked and murmured to him in the familiar old way I always had before. He began to relax. Finally he made a little bit of a hum, the tiniest one possible, and then lay as he always had, singing his lovely song. I leaned back against the bed and held him, stroking and stroking and stroking. A great familiar contentment came over us both. "You see, everything is just the same as before Deecher came," I told him. I explained to him all over again about Deecher and the city and how miserable he had been there. Surely he must understand how terrible it would be for an animal to go to a place like a jail and be locked up. "There is a big, ugly word for what they do to animals in the city, but I can't remember it," I said. "It means being locked up until they die. So you see, poor Deecher—"

He hummed and hummed, and I really thought he might understand.

"I missed you while I was gone," I whispered. "I didn't want to go without you at all, but what could I do? You don't like going in the car, remember? Did you think maybe I was never coming back—and then that huge animal came with me—"

How terrible it must have seemed to him, I thought. Suppose Mother and Dad went off, and I was left alone and didn't know where they had gone or whether they would come back again? And then suppose I heard them coming home and ran to meet them, and there was a terrible, strange giant covered with long brown hair? And then suppose he began making those hideous barks, and I heard him all day long?

"Poor little Jiggs!" He looked up at me with his eyes contented, half closed, and sang louder and louder. "I see how you felt," I said. "And you're so little and he's so big. I'm even a little bit scared of him; he's bigger than I am when he stands up and jumps." I tried to imagine what it would be like to be only six inches high. I put my head down on the floor and looked up. What a strange world it was, under the bed, with coils of springs and bedclothes hanging down. All shadowy. The room looked huge, as big as a circus tent when you thought about being so little. I tried to think how big Deecher would seem to me if I were six inches high, like Jiggs. I would come halfway up his leg. . . . He would be a giant about twenty times as high as I was, I thought. Imagine! His nose alone, with those big long teeth, would be half as long as every bit of me.

"I really see how you feel," I said fervently.

Helen came in to change her dress. "Are you just talking to that cat?" she asked. "I thought Carol must be up here."

"I was telling him about Deecher," I said. "He's scared."

She laughed. "Honestly, you'd think he was a *person*. As if a cat can understand talk."

When she came in, Jiggs had stood up in my lap, kneading his feet nervously and eyeing the open door. Suddenly Deecher began to bark again, and he leaped from my hands and disappeared back under the bed.

Angrily I ran downstairs. Deecher was making a terrible noise, barking and barking. "Jiggs won't eat or anything when Deecher barks," I said to Mother. "Why did he go and start barking again?"

When I looked outside, though, I could see why. He was playing the Game. He always barked like that when he played the Game, and I had thought it was wonderful, a part of the fun. Now Claude was showing how he could play, performing for his two best friends. Deecher had never looked so fine or leaped so high or barked so loud. The boys were impressed. "Boy, oh boy, what a dog!" they said.

I actually forgot all about Jiggs for a while, then, while I watched Deecher and the boys. They took turns holding the stick. I guess Deecher was so glad to be free that he really outdid himself. It must have been half an hour before I remembered Jiggs. Oh, dear, all that time Deecher had been barking and Jiggs shivering under the bed. I rushed back upstairs.

So it was all to do over. Mother called after a while and said it was my turn to go for the milk. She wanted a pint of cream too. "I'll bring you fresh milk," I promised

Jiggs, crouching down on the floor to peer at him. "Maybe you can have some cream—I'll ask Mother. Wait—I'll be back right away—"

His eyes looked at me, unblinking. Of course he would wait, I thought, he would wait and wait and *wait* there under the bed. He couldn't possibly come out into the lovely world now, when that huge fierce animal was there. Even now Deecher was barking. There had been those terrible sounds all day. . . . I had such a sympathetic lump in my throat that I could hardly speak when I got downstairs. It was actually a kind of soreness, as if I had my tonsils back.

When I got to Hansen's, Ralph was coming from the barn with the milk. I stood watching him put it in the milkroom, and Sister Hansen came to strain it and get part of it ready for the separator. I loved watching the separator go, it seemed such a miracle that plain milk went into the big kettle at the top, and soon skim milk came from one little spout and yellow cream from the other.

"How is Jiggs?" Sister Hansen asked right away. She always asked and I had told her how wonderful and clever he was.

I told her this time about the dog and about how Jiggs had acted all that day. She listened sympathetically, and then she said, "Sometimes cats are like that. It's all or nothing."

The lump filled my throat again, and I had to swallow hard before I could ask, "What shall I do?"

"Maybe he'll get used to it," she said. "Likely he will. I remember when Tab was upset because we let another cat in the kitchen. She never minded the dogs or the birds, but she would not have another cat. It's jealousy, that's what it is. But when he finds out you aren't going to be any different—" She smiled at me and handed me a small bottle of cream she had taken from the littlest spout. "He'll be all right."

"I'm going to give him some of this cream," I said.

But even Sister Hansen's rich yellow cream was not enough to bring Jiggs out from under that bed. He refused to touch it, even when I dragged him to the dish. He refused milk as well. After supper, when Deecher had been quiet for a long time, I brought up some scraps of meat, something Jiggs usually loved. But he refused to touch that too. He refused to move. All night long he crouched under the bed. Next morning, he was asleep, curled tight.

"I'll feed him when he wakes up," Mother said. "Hurry, or you'll be late for school."

"Maybe he's sick," Mother said. "Maybe it's not just Deecher after all."

We both knelt on the floor of my room after school. "I just don't believe a cat would refuse to eat for two whole days unless he was sick. Maybe he ate something he shouldn't while we were away."

"Carol says he ate fine—just milk—"

"Anyway, I think we should take him to the doctor or you'll be sick again yourself," Mother said, and patted my hand.

So we dragged Jiggs out and carried him off to Dr. Cox, the veterinarian. He was an old friend of our family, the same way the regular doctor was, and the dentist. Everybody knew everybody in our town. He knew all about Jiggs, of course. "Well, well, let's see," he said, rubbing his hands together. "Let's have him here on the table."

Jiggs cowered and spat as Dr. Cox examined him. He looked more terrified than ever. He was trembling all over, especially when his temperature was taken.

"He has a little bit of temperature, not enough to bother him," the doctor said. "I don't see a thing wrong with him. Has he had a bad scare or anything? Or it may be he has some worms. We could try pills for that, they can't hurt him."

So he gave us some pills and showed us how to make Jiggs swallow one. It seemed quite easy as he did it himself, stroking Jigg's throat and holding his mouth shut while I held his paws together. He had had plenty of practice with all the different animals he took care of in our town. "Give him one tomorrow morning and one tomorrow night," he said. "No food until the next day."

Jiggs looked terrible. He looked a thousand times sicker now than when we had brought him to the doctor, and a lot more scared. The minute we got home he was under the bed again.

To tell us to give those pills was easy. To give them was another matter.

Mother helped me. She tried holding the paws and I tried putting the pill in Jiggs' mouth when I finally pried it open. Prying a kitten's mouth open isn't easy, especially with those sharp teeth. He began to struggle when I tried putting the pill far back in his throat, as Dr. Cox had done, and my own teeth were set so hard together they ached afterward. Suddenly he got his paws away from Mother and scratched her, hard, across the back of her hand. She gave him a quick slap. The pill flew out of his mouth.

I began to cry. "I can't make him—I can't! He'll hate me!"

Mother looked at her hand and looked at me and looked at Jiggs, slowly, from one to the other. "Do you hate me for giving you pills?" she asked. "When you know it's for your own good?"

"Jiggs doesn't know it's for his good," I said. "How can he? And anyway—" I felt all mixed up. Actually, I

did remember thinking I hated Mother because she gave
me pills. "How could a cat know about pills?" I asked.
"He's never had to know about being sick—or about anything *awful*—" I glared toward the porch, where Deecher
had chosen just that minute to begin barking.

Jiggs gave a mighty struggle, but the two of us held on.

"All the same," Mother said grimly, "we'd better get
this pill down before you go to school. It's a two-woman
job." She put on gloves that came up over her wrists and
I held Jiggs, petting him and stroking him for a while before we tried again. At last it disappeared, that terrible
pill, and Jiggs went streaking off upstairs to feel sorry
for himself under the bed. And to hate me, I thought, to
be hating me all day long.

Mother said, "You're going to be late," and handed
me my books. She leaned quickly and gave me a kiss.
"Maybe even cats must learn about awful things some
time," she said.

The minute I got home for lunch I went upstairs and
was relieved to find Jiggs sleeping in his own little bed.
Something about the pill had made him sleep, Mother
thought, which seemed a good thing. Sometimes you
could just sleep away a sickness, I knew, especially a little
cold or an upset stomach, if it wasn't too upset. I tiptoed
out, and before I went back to school I looked in at him
again. There he lay, looking sweet and soft and wrinkling
his nose, almost smiling, in his sleep. I wanted to touch
him. I wished that he were sleeping on my lap and I could
run my finger around his neck and into the incredible
softness under his chin. But I did not disturb him. I went
quietly away and school was better that afternoon.

In fact, a very exciting thing happened.

We had, in our town, a Light Opera Company. It was
organized "for people who like to sing together," I re-

member. It was one of those attempts to make village life a little richer for a few special people. My teacher that year, Mrs. Boyden, belonged to it. I had seen her perform several times, with pride and admiration. She was pretty and plump and red-cheeked and black-haired. People felt sorry for her because her young husband had died in the war, and she had to teach to take care of her little boy. But she was always gay, and the music in our room was the best part of everybody's day. She took charge of the school chorus as well, and it was considered a great privilege to belong to it.

The day we gave Jiggs the pill, Mrs. Boyden asked three girls and three boys in our class to stay after school for a "very special meeting." As eager as I was to get home and see how Jiggs was doing, I was curious to know what we were wanted for. And it turned out to be a lovely thing. She was to take the leading part in a light opera about gypsies, and there had to be some gypsy children in it, along with a cast and chorus of adults. She wanted us to take these parts. We would have one line to speak, each of us, and would sing with several of the choruses.

"It will mean a lot of practice," she said. "And it will mean staying out rather late for a few nights, because we have two performances here and two out in the county."

We were enchanted. Imagine—traveling actors! We would be "on the road" like a circus.

"I've told your parents all this in these letters. And about the costumes too. We don't have much money, so everybody provides his own. It will mean work for your mothers and some money from your fathers. So you must talk it all over with them tonight. I need the answers as soon as possible." She smiled at us. "I've chosen you six because you have the best voices and because none of you are behind in any of your work at school." She looked severe, then, and added, "I've promised the principal that none of you will get behind in your work. You can see how much work that means."

I was so excited delivering that letter and the news to Mother that I forgot all about Jiggs when I got home. I bragged to my sisters and to Carol: "Maybe I'll decide to be an opera star instead of a poet."

"Well, maybe we won't have to hear any more poetry," Claude said when he heard this.

But Helen was not so pleased. "What if we have to start listening to her *sing?*"

Mother frowned at them both. "A family helps each member," she said severely. "How in the world can you expect anybody to believe in you if nobody does in your own house?"

I went to meet Dad to get in the first word, before Mother could think of objections to tell him. But it was not until after supper that I finally had the consent of both. They had doubted whether the late hours would be good for me, and the extra work. They doubted whether I could keep my lessons up. Before they said "yes" I was certain that everybody was going to be allowed to be in that operetta but me. One by one, they telephoned the good news, and when I had my permission I had to call them all back again. Finally I went up to bed, still far too excited to think of sleep.

And there was Jiggs, sitting on his little bed, washing himself. He ran to me, mewing, and I knew with a terrible pang of guilt that he was hungry. But oh, dear, he was still supposed to have another pill. I hadn't even remembered to change his box that day.

I couldn't bear the idea of another struggle like the last, and not only for his sake. If only it could be Dad instead of Mother who came to tuck me up; he might forget all about Jiggs and that other pill, and then I could slip downstairs when everybody was settled and get him some good supper.

"Sssh!" I begged him. "If you don't stop making such a fuss you'll have to take a pill."

But I did not reckon with Mother. She never forgot a pill in her whole life. She came upstairs with her gloves on. "It's doctor's orders," she always said about any medicine. "If you're not going to do as the doctor says, why call one?"

Jiggs saw the gloves and went scooting under the bed.

"He's all better," I said. "All he needs is a good supper, and he'll be—"

"Get him out of there," Mother said firmly. "There's no use getting him half well and then being cowardly."

So I had to crawl under the bed again and drag him out. He dug in and his claws scraped along the rug. "Please, Jiggs, this is the last one," I told him, and we held him prisoner. Before we could get the pill down, Gerry had to hold his hind legs and I his front legs while Mother pried his mouth open. I crooned "Jiggsy, Jiggsy," all the time, talking baby talk as people seem to do in a crisis with children or animals. "Tomorrow you can have cream —and salmon—"

"Tomorrow he can have good plain nourishing milk," Mother said. "He'll need simple food to get well, the way you did." She had the pill far back in his throat and stroked to get it down, with his mouth held tight. Jiggs gulped. "There, it's down!"

The minute we let him go, he was deep in his corner again. I went down on my knees and peered at him; I could see only his wide eyes. "Come get in your little bed—"

"Get in your own. He's all right where he is," Mother said. "Honestly, the troubles with that cat! I saw Sister Hansen uptown today, and I told her if I'd known—" She saw my stricken face. "No, I didn't tell her she could have him back," she said, and laughed and tucked the covers in around me. "You're more trouble than Jiggs is, goodness knows, and I never think of sending *you* back. Do I?"

"After everybody is asleep, I'll get him out and comfort him," I thought. But I was too tired. The next thing I knew Jiggs was nudging me awake in the morning sun. He wanted his breakfast. I flew downstairs after it, and what a joy to see him eat. He emptied his bowl without once looking up, his tongue flicking so fast it could hardly be seen. When I went off to school I was in such high spirits one would have thought I was a singing gypsy child already.

It was weeks before Deecher was settled happily with us. But at last he seemed at home, free and satisfied, able to see cows going by and horses and wagons and herds of sheep without going out of his mind with excitement. After a time we never tied him up. Dad and Claude built him a fine big house.

The idea of Deecher and Jiggs being friends was still in my mind. It would be so pretty, the big brown dog and the little yellow cat eating side by side. Once, in a carnival, I had seen a cat riding on a dog's back, and I had a notion I might train them eventually and become famous and rich and travel all over America. DEECHER AND JIGGS, THE FAMOUS DOG * CAT TEAM! Maybe we could join a circus. I told Carol she could go along.

But every time I tried to bring those two together, Jiggs puffed himself out like a ripe milkweed and began to spit. He wouldn't stay any longer than he had to in the same room. Deecher only looked pained and turned his eyes in another direction, as if the sight of such a silly animal was more than he could bear.

Practices for the operetta began after Christmas and soon we had to go every single day. There were twenty-five in the company, and the six Chosen Ones felt terribly important to be working with grownups. The director gave us ice cream cones every single day. Then Mother began working on my costume, and my full red skirt was so wonderful that I went whirling through the house in it, upsetting everything, and decided to be a ballerina.

During that busy time, having so much to do and my lessons besides, I am afraid I spent very little time with poor Jiggs. For a while I simply did not need him. But one day—it was the day of the first performance, a sort of tryout matinee—I came home after dark to find Mother worried.

"Jiggs acted funny this morning," she said, "and kept crying to get out. He walked back and forth, making the most awful racket at the door, and scratching things. I thought maybe he was sick, but he ate all right. And then, when I opened the door, he simply flew past me—and past Deecher too. And over the back fence—"

Instantly I was in a panic. He had never gone out of the dooryard before except when I took him myself.

"Once I thought I saw him in that old apple tree you and Carol play in," Mother said. "But he doesn't seem to be there now."

I rushed around the house to look.

The apple tree Mother meant was a grand, gnarled old fellow we called "the 24-ounce" because it was supposed to bear apples that weighed so much. Often, in summer, Carol and I played in it the whole day. Once we made a telephone exchange, I remember, stringing lines from one limb to another with a system of little bells. Several times I took Jiggs up with us, and he loved climbing around on the big limbs and stretching out to sleep in patches of sun. Mother objected to taking him up a tree; he might learn about birds and hunt them afterward. But I thought he might learn about birds and love them. That's how special I thought he was, and how different from other cats.

"Jiggs, kitty, kitty, kitty!" I called beneath the dark tree. How different it looked at night, I thought, how mysterious and shadowy. I was sure that if Jiggs was there I would be able to see his light coat and his luminous eyes. I went all around the lot, looking in every tree. After a time Claude brought his big flashlight out to help me. Gerry brought a warm scarf and Mother's injunction to put it on. Helen brought a dish of salmon to try to tempt him. "He could smell salmon clear from upstairs, remember?" I loved her for it.

Our jibes and teasing were never really bad blood between us; we were only, as in all families, letting off steam that couldn't be let off anywhere but at home. The important thing was that we were always together, solidly, in an emergency.

My two sisters stood with me that night, while I called and called, one on either side. The night was large and dark around us, and we held hands, in a row. The noises of a town have a strange, hollow sound on a winter evening. Mothers calling their children sounded far away. Suddenly a cat gave one of those unearthly screeches, at a distance, in the direction of Hansen's barn.

"That couldn't be Jiggs!" I cried. "Could it?"

We listened and I felt my heart sinking and cold, and said, "It wasn't his voice—"

"Voices aren't the same when you yell," Helen said. She meant it kindly, but I began to shiver.

"Why should he yell? Unless he's hurt?" I asked.

Our fingers tightened, and I realized for the first time that the rest of my family loved Jiggs too.

We went to the very end of our big lot, which was a quarter-block, like most of the lots in old Utah villages. Behind the house itself was a flower garden and then a

vegetable garden and small orchard and then the buildings, much used by the farmer who had lived there before we came. There was a granary and a chicken coop
and a pigpen and a sheep corral, besides the huge empty
barn. We could climb to a window, high over the lofts,
and look down on our neighbors' world of animals and
birds.

In the door of the barn I called again and again, my
voice echoing among the dark rafters.

"It's different in here at night," Gerry said, clutching my
fingers.

We stood silent. I began to call again. But then we
heard Dad coming, calling us for supper. He was waiting
at the back gate.

"Don't you worry," he said. "That cat'll come home
when he gets good and hungry."

"Why should he run away?" I asked, in guilty despair.

Deech was lying comfortably on the rug by the warm
stove. He had begun to come into the house more and
more as it got colder outside, and all of us enjoyed having
him there. A big dog is a cozy thing in a house in wintertime.

"Jiggs never got to sleep by the stove," I said, needing
to blame somebody. "Deecher is always there and Jiggs
hates him." I glared at the poor dog, who looked up when
he heard me speak his name. For a minute, I hated him
too. "It's all Deecher's fault!"

"Jiggs can sleep by the stove any old time he wants to,"
Claude said. "Deecher wouldn't care."

Of course it was true. I knew that. But I did not want
to blame Jiggs and I did not want to blame myself. The
truth was that I had not paid any attention to Jiggs lately,
and this hurt my conscience bitterly. I had fed him later
and later. I had forgotten to change his box. I had been
coming so late from practice that I had not taken time

to hold him. Worst of all, I had stopped coming home at the time he expected me. Sadly I remembered how he used to be waiting every single day at the door.

"That *darn* operetta!" I said.

Mother looked at me. "You wanted to be in it, I seem to remember," she said. "You won't be the only one to be glad when it's over."

There are times when the whole world goes wrong. That was such a time for me. After supper I wanted to go back out to look and my sisters offered to go with me again. But Mother ordered us to our lessons. Claude offered to look, but Dad said, "We'll all go in the morning. I'll set the clock early—"

Try as I might, though, I could not study. I kept listening around the edge of the story in my reader, and around the numbers I was supposed to add and subtract and multiply and divide. After a time I fell asleep over my papers, and Dad picked me up and carried me upstairs. Yet, as sleepy as I had been before I went to bed, I could not sleep once I got into it. I lay listening to the voices downstairs. They were laughing. How could they laugh tonight? I looked at Jiggs' empty bed and wondered where he might be, out in the immense and dangerous dark. I heard Deecher being let out, heard him bark at a late passer-by.

"Even if Jiggs wanted to come home, he wouldn't dare," I thought bitterly. That hateful dog. If he had never come—

Just then I would rather blame Deecher than the show. How exciting it had been to get my face painted and my hair slicked down and oiled black, and to dress in my bright costume. I loved the strange and female feeling of earrings dangling against my cheeks. We had been permitted to look out at the audience through a tiny hole in the curtain. And then—to see the faces of the audience when we came on stage! The roll of laughter, the patter of clapping. Before the curtain parted I had felt almost the way I did before diving into a pool.

When I finally fell asleep, I was thinking about the show and about what fun it would be to go out of town and have supper in a restaurant. But in the middle of the night I suddenly woke, thinking of Jiggs. I seemed to have heard him in a dream.

A wind brushed at the curtains and I saw that there was a moon driving through black clouds. I got up and crept to the window. The world was big and silent and cold and the sky was endless and wild. Stars winked in and out. Where was Jiggs, out there? Was he cold? And hungry and afraid? I doubt whether I have ever felt more lonely than I did that night.

Then I heard his voice.

Was it? I ceased to breathe, but heard only the wind blowing. Was that—again? The wind made so much noise I couldn't be sure. Maybe he was at the door, downstairs, wanting to get in. I rushed, barefoot, into the dark hall and down the stairs and into the kitchen. I flung open the door. He wasn't there.

But Mother was. She found me standing with the wind blowing over me and through the house.

"What on earth are you doing?"

"I thought I heard Jiggs—"

"And no slippers! Do you want to catch your death of cold?"

I began to cry and tremble and she called Dad and together they bundled me up and gave me hot milk and I spent the rest of the night on the davenport, in a warm room with a lingering fire.

The next thing I remember, Claude was shaking me. "Jiggs is up on the roof," he said.

"I knew I heard him! I told Mother—" I scrambled upstairs and into my clothes. By the time I got outside Claude was on a ladder against the back of the house. Jiggs was peering over a rainpipe, big-eyed and bedraggled, the wind blowing his fur into ridges and ruffs.

Deecher barked with excitement, and Jiggs fled higher. So into the house with the horrible dog. Everybody was concerned with the one in peril now.

Our ladder wasn't long enough. We had to borrow one from a house painter down the street, and it took all four of us kids to carry it home and set it up. By the time Claude climbed up, Jiggs had retreated up the roof, and sat shivering by the chimney.

"Be careful!" Mother cried again and again. And to me, "No, you can't climb up, you just stay right where you are. If he falls. . . . Oh, *that cat!*"

I stood with no eyes for anything or anybody but Jiggs, a bowl of milk ready in my hands.

What a job it was to get him down! Claude had to edge over the roof in the brisk wind, and I watched him with love and terror. He finally got Jiggs by the scruff of the neck and dragged him carefully along to the top of the ladder. "Now, catch him," he called. "Don't let him get away."

I set the milk down and stretched out my coat like a fire net. Jiggs came sprawling into it. For a minute he struggled, but I had him. Safe in the house, I held him by the fire until he was warm and calm again. Then he ate, passionately, as if he were half-starved.

"You'll never run away again, will you? It was awful, wasn't it, out there in the night?" I whispered.

I had never hated so much to leave him and go to school. When I came home, running all the way, Mother said he had slept the whole day. I did my lessons in no time at all, one eye on his bed. When he sat up at last and ate and washed himself, he looked more beautiful than ever before.

That night I went happily off to the theater with my friends and could enjoy completely the excitement of the show. How I sang! I had one line, and when I said it the family clapped. Everybody's family clapped, which made a grand and successful thing out of every village show.

From then on, all the performances melt together in my memory. We gave one more at home and four in other towns nearby. Each time I came home, late and weary, Jiggs was there to welcome me and to curl up against me and help me get calm and warm. Until the very last one—

I came in full of excitement and chatter about the show and the dessert we had been served afterward and the drive home in a school bus through the night. "We all sang, the whole way. And Mr. Johnson said we've made enough money to buy a bass horn for the high-school band."

Mother said kindly, "That's wonderful. But now calm down and get to bed. Tomorrow's another day." I heard her say to Dad, as I went into the bathroom, "Thank goodness, that's the end of that."

I was brushing my teeth, the door a little ajar, when I heard Dad say, "For heaven's sakes, I hope she doesn't notice tonight. Morning's soon enough."

"She'll notice all right—"

I stood suddenly frozen. I knew what it had to be I would be sure to notice. I opened the door wide and asked, "What? Is it about Jiggs?"

It was. Once more, he had got away.

He never really came home again.

But he was not quite lost to me. In a way, what happened next was the best part of our whole friendship. In a very special way.

For a while, my sisters and I went out on a search every single day. We carried Jiggs' bowl of milk with us, or sometimes salmon, or trout heads after Claude had been fishing. Jiggs preferred those to anything else. He always carried them lovingly around the house, to Mother's dismay; she would find them under cushions and behind doors, horribly gaping and smelly. "He hides them," she complained, "like a puppy hides bones."

Never once did Jiggs answer my call. Twice my brother thought he saw him, once by the woodpile when he was getting the kindlings in, and once in the big empty barn. At last I decided to leave the dish outside in a sheltered place, under the granary, which was built off the ground on thick logs. The food disappeared, and I had a ray of hope, though of course I did not know whether Jiggs had got it. Somehow, though, I had a feeling that he did, so I began to fill the dish each day. It was, after all, the only thing left for me to do for him. Mother thought it was a waste, that I was likely feeding strays and even encouraging rats in the granary. But I would not have missed doing it for the world, especially after I thought I caught sight of him one day as Gerry and I took the dish into the yard.

Perhaps, I thought, if I had been alone he would have come to me. He had never really been a pet to anybody else. He had never been willing to sit on my sisters' laps very long, but had jumped down and come to me the moment I appeared. I had been proud of this, as if it proved that I was a good person, worth his love. There is nothing like being *chosen*, after all.

The next day Gerry started out with me. "You stay and guard the door," I said to her, in a way I had learned. If she was not to go on insisting on something, you had to provide her with something else to do, something that made her feel useful and important. "See that Deecher doesn't get out, see? You know what happens when he barks, don't you? I might be just on the *edge* of getting Jiggs to come—"

"I want to go with you," she said.

"You remember that time we almost got Jiggs down from the roof and then Deecher barked and he ran clear up by the chimney?" I asked.

She nodded, and finally agreed. I left her standing firmly against the kitchen door.

It was an April evening. The cool shadows had begun to grow long under the trees. I could smell the lilac buds as I passed the bushes, a little wet from a small rain that afternoon, and intensely sweet. The ground, just touched with rain, had that rainy-dusty fragrance that is like nothing else. I walked in the sparkle of the air, that special sparkle that is more wonderful in high mountains than anywhere in the world. It is odd how well I remember all of this, how I closed the barnyard gate after me, how I turned toward the granary, and how suddenly, I saw Jiggs break from the shadows where I always left his dish. He ran, leaping, across the yard and vanished into the barn.

So he did come. Now I knew for sure. Excited, I got his dirty dish and washed it at the pump in the barnyard. I kept my eye on the barn and felt that he was watching me. Had he been watching me every night, I wondered, while I washed his dish? How glad I was that I had not failed him!

The sky had begun to go red, and I remember how lovely the water looked, full of reflections. I went back to the sheltered place by the granary and set the dish down and filled it with milk. And when I looked back at the barn, I saw Jiggs sitting in the high window, perfectly plain, in the last of the sun. He did not move, only sat looking down.

I did not move either. For a long moment we looked at each other.

Then I thought, "If I sit here by the dish, he might come to me." I sat down, watching.

Jiggs sat. I sat. He was waiting for me to go, but I was waiting for him to come. If only Gerry would be patient, I thought, if only she would really guard that door. I felt that if Deecher should bark I could not bear it. I would hate him forever.

But he was quiet. And nobody came.

The sun lowered. The shadows changed. For a time the barn looked rosy-brown in the sunset light, the lines of the boards and all of the knotholes plain. As the sky color altered, it seemed orange and yellow and then purple and blue, and finally dark brown again. It was one of those slow sunsets one gets sometimes when there is a bank of clouds in the west.

At last the deep blue lay everywhere and dusk gathered around me like a curtain. Jiggs still sat, now only a light spot on the great dark bulk of the barn. "Well, I can sit as long as you can," I whispered, willing him to come.

A star appeared and I made a wish on it, whispering the words under my breath. "Star light, star bright, first star I see tonight, I wish I may, I wish I might, have the wish I wish tonight." I did not have to think the words of my wish, that Jiggs would not be afraid, that he would come; the strength of my feeling was the wish. Perhaps he would think I had gone away when it got quite dark, and then come to get his supper. I knew, agonized, why he would not come to me. He thought I would imprison him, that I would take him in the house and keep him there again. He thought he would have to be in the same room with that terrible dog.

I remembered with sorrow how I had dragged him from under the bed, how he had his temperature taken and then was forced to swallow huge and bitter pills. How I had failed to come home, failed to change his box, failed to bring his supper. How I had tried to get him to eat from a dish set beside Deecher's on the floor.

But I remembered all the good things too. Surely he must remember them. How warm and nice it was in his little bed, how he lay on my lap by the fire, how he came to wake me in the morning, how we played games among the quilts and in the tree, how he liked his ball and his bell and the catnip mouse I gave him for Christmas. From where I sat, wishing him to come, I tried to make him remember.

At last he moved. He walked across the window, watching. And then he disappeared.

I hardly breathed. There was such a stillness in me, in my listening, that every sound was exaggerated. I could hear the neighbors coming to their barns and going away. Doors opened and slammed. Somebody was singing. The stallion was running around and around, I could hear the rhythmic beating of his great hooves. The sky was suddenly filled with stars, even though there lingered a pale light in the western sky.

Jiggs suddenly appeared in the barn door. He seemed very large, his tail trailing around the doorsill after him. It was odd how clearly I could see him, but I was accustomed to the dusk and he was the color of gold. He started to walk toward me and I could see his eyes. He stopped once, and so did my heart. Then he took one step, another, slowly and cautiously. His tail was waving from side to side, his ears pointed, his head up. How beautiful he was! Another step, graceful and delicate—another—another—

I prayed that Deecher would not bark. That no one would call.

The birds had been singing in the bright way they do at dusk, from every tree. But even they seemed suddenly to abandon every sound and every motion, as if they understood how it was with me and waited too. I could see how dangerous Jiggs might be for them, as a hunger, for he came in a silence that was absolute. He stood a few feet away at last, and looked at me, one paw lifted, as though he meant to fly if I made a move. It was terrible not to move, but I did not. Another step. I felt curious little ripples of nerves in my arms and legs. I was sitting tight, as they say, on my crossed legs, and they went to sleep under me. I longed to move, to stretch, but made no motion at all. Why must he be so slow? He reached his dish, a few inches from my hand. Tentatively, he tried the milk, and looked at me again. For a moment I suffered his distrust. But then—I remember the joy of my relief—he settled down on his haunches and began to eat. He made the familiar cozy lapping sound as he ate, his tongue flashing in and out. He did not look at me again until he had emptied the dish and washed it all around, with his tongue, exactly as he had always done. Then, glancing at me now and then, he began to wash himself.

One paw and then another, his face, all around himself. Should I reach out and touch him? I wanted to, terribly, but did not dare. Mother would call soon, I knew it, and then it would be over. It was my turn to go for the milk. If only I could touch him, just once, to show him that I would not hurt him, or force him, or imprison him.

He stopped washing and sat looking at me. Then, in his graceful swinging way, he came to me and moved along my side. I trembled. He made a low familiar mewing and stepped, gingerly, a little stiffly, into my lap. At first he stood awkwardly, treading with his feet in a funny way I remembered very well, as if he searched for a steady spot. I touched his fur—barely touched—then more firmly, saying his name. And at last he settled himself, he gave me his full weight. As he lay, curled comfortably, the ritual of stroking began. I dared now to stretch out, and leaned against one of the logs in such comfort as I had never known.

He began to hum. To sing. His song trembled under my hand and he laid down his head. It seemed to me he sighed—I have been told that cats do not sigh, but why shouldn't they?—and I told him all my news. How I had missed him, how empty his bed seemed, how I hated Deecher for driving him away.

He closed his eyes. I leaned down and put my cheek against his fur. It was a warm night; for a little while we dozed together.

Then the kitchen door slammed. Somebody called my name. Jiggs jerked up his head and his fur swelled. The gate opened. He leaped lightly from my lap and was gone. I saw the streak of his going, but it was all right. I knew how to reach him now. I was satisfied.

That was the first time. There were many more times that spring. As the days lengthened I went later and later to see him. There is no o'clock for dusk, and dusk was the hour he expected me. "We tell time by the sun, like the Indians," I told him. He was always watching for me in that window of the barn. He never made a motion or a sound up there; one would have thought he was made of stone, a statue set into a niche.

When I had washed his dish and sat down to wait, he simply vanished from the window. And came in silence. It was always the same.

"Where on earth have you been?" Mother asked several times.

I never told her, or even Carol. I don't know why, exactly. It seemed to me that if nobody knew then nobody could interfere. People and dogs and problems had spoiled everything for Jiggs and me before; I was not going to let them do it again. The secret had to be kept, like a secret formula in a fairy tale. I found a little jar in which I put milk (or sometimes cream, when I could get away with some) secretly, and a covered dish for bits of fish and meat, often saved from my plate. I always returned to the house peaceful and quiet and full of joy.

When something interfered at dusk, I went later, through the warm summer nights. Once the moon was rising as I came, and Jiggs stepped across the yard touched with light, his eyes shining. We felt safe in the dark, both of us, and I think he must have liked it as much as I did. Anyway, he always came, and whether for food or love, who knows? Why not for both? Whether early or late, I never missed going. The first time I was late far past sunset and dusk, I said, "Time can be told by the stars and the moon." I still felt quite certain that he understood every word I said and everything I meant to say.

It was in early July that my father announced something exciting one night at supper. He had a holiday and we were going to Fish Lake to stay in the cabin of some good friends. We had the place offered to us for a *whole week!* It was on a blue lake, one of the most beautiful lakes in the Rocky Mountains, and we would have a little boat to use every day. We would be able to climb mountain trails. We would sleep on open porches under moonlit peaks. We would sit around campfires and sing together with our guitars. It was the holiday we all loved better than any other.

But suddenly I thought, in the midst of the excitement, "What about Jiggs? He expects me now—"

That night I told him. I would be back soon. Only a week—only seven nights—and I would come back and then everything would be the same. He must understand. He must wait patiently for me. I told him I would leave some extra food at the granary the last morning, to help tide him over.

The last night before we left I took him an especially good supper. A big supper, because while sandwiches were being made for the trip I managed to slip away bits of tuna fish and several kinds of meat. We were very contented and talked together for a long time. I told him I would save all the fish heads the last day at the lake and bring them back to him. That time I even brought out his old catnip mouse to keep him company while I was gone.

At last I was called, and he leaped up to go.

"Good-by!" I called after him, and watched him out of sight. He turned briefly at the door, stood looking at me, before he vanished into the dark barn.

Surely he knew how to get some food for himself now, I thought. I knew there were mice in the barn. So I went to the house and joined in the preparations for our holiday with the greatest joy. We left before dawn, loaded with supplies. The last thing I did was rush out to the granary with a little cache.

It could not have been a happier holiday, and the fish were biting marvelously. Even I caught fish, though I was usually too impatient for good fishing. I never saw the tails and heads left on our plates every day without thinking of Jiggs at home. Deecher came right along with us, and as much as I hated him sometimes, I had to love him on a holiday. He added to an excursion as a cat could never do. He scouted the trails ahead as we tramped and chased chipmunks and discovered porcupines. One of the dogs in the camp got a noseful of needles, and we were proud that Deecher was clever enough to bark and keep his distance. He never seemed to tire. At night he guarded our cabin, and we felt safe with him beside us when we walked around the lake in the moonlight.

Dogs have certain ways, I thought, feeling disloyal, and cats have others. One can love them both for what they are. Why should it be necessary to hate them because sometimes they are each other's enemies?

Yet it was because of Jiggs that I was glad to see the last day come. Carefully I wrapped the fish heads and tucked them secretly among my things, hoping Mother would not find them. All the way home I thought of how I would go out and take them that very night. No matter how late, I would go. As soon as possible, Jiggs should know that I was home.

We arrived at dusk and I was impatient to get away. But I helped unpack, not—as Mother thought—to be helpful, but to get out the present that I had promised Jiggs. As soon as I got at it, I slipped away.

I was disappointed, but of course not surprised, that Jiggs was not waiting in his window. I got the dish ready, watching the barn, and then sat down to wait. No sign. It was no wonder, I thought, and imagined how he had come when I was away, prowling about his empty dish. So I went to the barn and stepped inside and called softly, "Jiggs—kitty, kitty, kitty!"

No sound. No motion. It would take time. Perhaps it would be as long as that first time, but it would be worth it in the end. I went back to the granary and made myself comfortable, sitting against the wall. Confidently, I waited. It felt good to be home again and to hear the familiar sounds of the neighborhood. After a time, I called again. Still no sign. It was not until Mother had called me several times, very crossly at last, that I finally gave up.

The next morning I hurried out to see whether the fish was gone. And it was. Every single head had disappeared. Good. Jiggs knew now that I was back and that everything would go on as before.

But that evening he still did not come.

The next night was my turn to get the milk. When I

came into Sister Hansen's kitchen, she said at once, "Your cat has been over here, at the barn."

"In *your* barn?" A wave of horror went over me.

"Yes. Ralph fed him with the others," she said.

"Is Ralph out there now?" I asked, and she said no, he had finished tonight.

I found him in the separator room. "Your mother says Jiggs has been in your barn," I said.

"Boy, oh boy, has he!" He laughed. "What a cat. He's got old Yellow Eyes going and coming."

My heart seemed to stop. "He doesn't *fight*, does he?"

"Sure he fights. He's the best old fighter in the bunch," he said. "At first he got beat up by a pair of them, but they already know who he is."

"But he's a *tame* cat," I said weakly.

"Well, Tab's his mother," Ralph said, "but Yellow Eyes was his dad, remember that. Maybe it's like Ma says, the old wild blood coming out." It seemed very funny to all of the Hansens, I found, that one of those kittens had "come home to roost."

When I got my milk, I pretended to start home and then circled the lot and went out to the barn. There was a row of cows, one with a little calf. It was a warm, living barn, full of chewing sounds and stamping and the rustling of hay. I stood in the half-opened door and called Jiggs' name, softly and hopefully. But there was no sign. I felt only the cows looking at me, for they all turned their heads.

I said nothing to the family. First I must believe it myself. When my brother wondered why I offered to take his turn to get the milk the next night, I said only, "They saw Jiggs—" and turned away. I could tell he understood.

Perhaps it was a mistake for me to go. But I had to do it. The suspense was terrible as Ralph set out the row of crocks. Then it was worse, as one cat appeared, and another, and another. Jiggs was the fourth to come.

"There he is," Ralph said.

As if I needed to be told! Jiggs was the same, only looking a little shaggy, and something was different about his walk. At first I thought he limped a little, but it was a kind of half-crouch, as if he were ready for an attack. I guess he was, too, though none of the cats interfered with him as he walked to a dish.

I longed to speak to him or touch him, but stood back in the shadows, waiting. When he finished I would call him, I thought. There was still a little milk left when he sat back on his haunches and began to wash, his back half-turned. By this time there were cats at every dish, and I wondered why old Yellow Eyes had not come. Suddenly another cat, one I had never seen before, appeared around a manger. He was coal black, with a funny brown patch over one eye. He stood looking for a while, his tail waving and his ears tense, and then slipped to Jiggs' dish and began to eat.

But he had scarcely got his tongue out of his mouth when Jiggs folded up and flew at him. They met head-on. It was as if the two of them stood on air for a second, a whirl of snarling fur. And then the other cat turned tail and fled.

I confess I had a flash of terrible pride as Jiggs sat calmly down again. His fur was ruffled and his tail as huge as it ever was for Deecher, but he began to smooth himself down.

Ralph was grinning at me. "See?"

I had no answer for him. I stooped, leaning forward, and said in a shaken voice, "Jiggs—kitty, kitty, kitty—"

He stopped washing and turned his head. For a minute he looked at me, I thought he meant to come. He stood up and took a step, and I stretched out my hand and spoke his name again. Ralph sat watching; I could hear him breathe. He had stopped milking and the barn was absolutely still. Until a cow lowed, as if it wondered. Jiggs crouched as I leaned down, waiting. But as my hand touched his fur, he began to swell and spit, exactly as he had done with Deecher every time. And as I began to stroke him, he gave a sudden snarling leap and I felt his claws along my wrist.

Then he was gone.

That is really the end of the story. For a while I did not lose hope entirely and put milk in the dish by the granary every night. But autumn came and winter came, and snow filled the dish, and finally it was lost under drifts that came halfway to the granary door. Our next-door neighbor asked us to go halves on a Jersey cow, and we did, so it was not necessary to go to Hansen's any more.

It was in February, almost my birthday again, the day Ralph spoke to me. I was taking off my wraps in the hall, I remember. He said, suddenly, behind me: "I saw that cat of yours last night."

I leaned down to unbuckle a boot, and the blood rushed to my head. "I thought you saw him almost every night." I did not want to talk about it; I spoke as if I did not care. When I saw his face I felt his look was malicious, as if he wished to nettle me.

"Not for quite a while now," he said. "But what I mean—"

His look told me, and my heart began to thump in my ears and the top of my head seemed to rise like a balloon on a string.

"He was dead. Found him in the loft when I went up to fork some hay."

I did not answer. I could not. For I did care. I cared so much that for a long moment I could barely move to draw away my other boot, or to stand again. My heart seemed to stop beating and when it began again it seemed to beat precariously, thinly, as if it hung by a spider's thread in my breast.

"But like Ma says," Ralph was going on cheerfully, "what difference does one cat make? Out of all—"

My stare must have stopped him. His ugly face floated in my tears. And the bell rang mercifully, and I turned and hurried away.

The Ghost

Because we lived in Manti from the time I was five, on the Sanpete line of the Denver and Rio Grande, I never saw a Negro until I was ten. When I did, on a trip with the family to see relatives in Denver, I was embarked upon my first journey into The World.

From Manti, we went to Provo on the smokey-pokey Sanpete line, and then boarded the long, sleek wonder that took us over the mountains, east. A sleeper was beyond our means—after all, there were six of us—but as we waited by the coach I watched with fascination the women in gloves and flowered hats who were getting onto curtained cars beyond. Mother had gloves, too, as if the train were a church, and all of us were in our Sunday best. Because Dad was a railroad man himself, officials in dark blue suits and gold-trimmed hats spoke to him and shook his hand. He talked with them too long entirely, though, for I was impatient to get aboard and was terrified that the panting engine would take offense and go steaming off without us.

"Let's get *on*, Daddy. Can we get on?"

In the midst of this fruitless imploring, I saw the Negro

for the first time. He was standing above us suddenly, at the top of the little row of steps, smiling down. He wore a spotless white coat with gold buttons.

"All right, up you come!" His voice was powerful and deep and he reached a hand for mine. I saw the flash of his white teeth before I turned, triumphant, to look down on the others. Then up came Gerry and Lulu. My brother, spurning help, followed us, and we all went to our place on the coach and the Negro tucked our bags safely over our heads, with our new coats folded neatly and our hats perched where they would not be crushed. By then Dad and Mother were safely aboard and the train gave a jerk and began to move.

It was wonderful from the first moment. Lulu insisted that my nose would be flat on top forever from the way I pressed it against the window every moment of my turn at the inside seat. Familiar places looked better seen from the moving train, for were we not superior to them all? Provo vanished at once, Springville was there like a wave of a wand, a flash of stones for the cemetery, a whiff of peavines from the factory, and I cried, "There's Maple Mountain! And Sierra Bonita—" Even the mountains were smaller from this moving window; we moved along their flanks at incredible speed. There, already, was the red glory of Spanish Fork Canyon.

"There's Castella!" We had gone there swimming one memorable picnic Sunday. It was a hot-springs resort run by the sister of Cyrus Dallin, Utah's most famous sculptor, he who had made the Angel Moroni on top of Salt Lake Temple and the Indian who stood in the rotunda of the Capitol. Years later I came to understand why Dallin came to spend his summers in his old home. His first figures had been molded of Utah clay, as had his immortal soul. He came back to renew himself with the rush of mountain water and the fruit of mountain land. Nowhere else, least of all in Boston, could one go in an hour from the tropic heat of the valley to the fragrant cool of a river running among pines. The profile of the mountains on the sky was the proper edge of his world, as of mine. All of us sing "O Ye Mountains High" in our fondest dreams.

"Imagine," Mother said, thinking of the same Sunday pleasures. "A great man like Cyrus Dallin handing out towels and bathing suits."

Later, returning from far-off places, I found Castella a shambles and finally there was nothing but a steamy puddle to show it had ever been a resort at all. Yet the canyon remains the same, a fantastic medley of colors every fall that unfolds fresh panoramas at every turn in the road.

"Utah is timeless," a poet once said to me when both of us were far from home. "It's exactly right for the resurrected Saints to come back to for the Millennium."

Almost at once the red-rocked glory of Spanish Fork Canyon was disappearing and the train stopped at the railroad town of Thistle before turning east.

Dad showed us other places he had worked as a young man; little wooden shacks beside the rights-of-way had once been busy because of the coal mines at Castle Gate and Helper and Price. "It'll be dark when we get to Price," Dad said, "and you'll go to sleep later and when you wake up it'll be Colorado." Except for a dip into Nevada and a trip to the Grand Canyon of Arizona, Colorado would be my first Other State, Denver my first great city besides Salt Lake.

"The mountains are higher in Colorado," Claude said, getting his statistics out.

"None of them are higher than Timp!" I cried. Our own mountain, Timpanogas, was for me the highest of all; we had climbed to snow on her back in the month of July, sliding down a glacier to the edge of an Emerald Lake bordered with primroses. Timp was beloved, an old friend forever at the windows of our rooms, so familiar it had a nickname just like the rest of us.

"Colorado has dozens of mountains higher than Timp," Claude said. But I turned my back on such heresy. Nothing on God's earth could ever be higher than Timp, that white majesty etched with pine. In summer it towered over V's of waterfalls and winding trails bright with flowers. It had a legend, too, that explained the existence of a great cave deep in its heart and the outline of a woman with flowing hair that made its profile on the sky. Once before I had turned my back on a Timp heresy; there was a rumor that the legend was composed by a white man and was not Ute Indian at all, and even that Timpanogas did not mean The Sleeping Woman in Ute, but Flowing Waters.

"Once," my mother said into my ear as I gazed out into the gathering dusk, "Dad and I came to Denver on this train in the wintertime. There was a moon shining on the snow in the high mountains and we could see deer standing among the pines. Like a Christmas card."

"They came to find something to eat by the right-of-way. Snow had covered everything they could reach," Dad said.

"Like that time they came to town and ate our bushes." I remembered seeing unlikely horns, one January morning, from my bedroom window.

Soon we could see the train winding on ahead, two engines making ready for the pull to come, and behind us, like a jointed caterpillar, came the mysterious and elegant cars with curtained windows. One was brighter than the others, and I could see white-coated Negroes moving about inside. The diner, where we ourselves would go for supper. I never heard a more wonderful sound than the gong coming down the aisle and the call, "Dinner is served. First call! Diner to the rear, please."

Everywhere Mother went became at once a home away

from home. To the washroom with us, every one, before we reeled gladly down the aisle toward the magic to the rear. "Let me open one—just once—" I implored my brother after the second set of heavy doors. I must be involved physically, head over heels; I must carry the packages. How I longed to be one of those to sleep in a high, green-curtained bed! Or like one woman we saw, to sit negligently in a tiny room with its own cunning washbasin, my eyes closed, an open book in my lap, the whole window mine if I cared to look. Outrageous that Mother should choose that moment to say, "Dad, you'd better do all the ordering. If you let *them*—" I knew she looked at me especially, but did not give her a glance, "—they'll order the most expensive things on the menu."

The last door opened onto steamy fragrance, and I ran my hand over a wall of gleaming aluminum. Glory Hallelujah! I was staggered by the white linen, the bright silver, flowers nodding on every table, even before our smiling, nodding black man led us to our own. For the first time in my life I was helped into my chair like a great lady. When he handed around a bouquet of menus, I saw his rosy palms and his marvelous, long fingers.

The dining car steward, like the conductor and brakeman, was familiar with my father and came at once to greet him. In his black suit he looked ready for a ball, and I wished my friends at home could see what a fine world this railroad world was, after all. In Mormon towns, a railroad man was a lesser being unless he happened to be a Bishop, which was Prince to a Deacon's Pauper. Dad had never advanced in the Holy Priesthood, even beyond the lowest order, a Deacon, which any boy of twelve could be. Until I grew up I never knew how to judge his sharp laughter at authority and pretense. There was one friend of his childhood whom he always met on the street with "*Hello, Deacon!*" and a roar of laughter, because they were the only two grown men in the valley who had remained so low.

Behind me the stiff-starched coat of the waiter brushed my chair. My father was given a pencil and paper on which to write our order. And then, suddenly, a devil in me caused me to look up from the menu and say in a loud voice, "*I want steak!*"

The steward and the waiter both smiled at me, but Dad's pencil stood in the air, outraged, and Mother gave me an angry glance.

"Ground beef—there is a supper of ground beef," Dad said firmly, as if he had not heard. *Supper*. Not even *dinner*.

"I hate ground beef," I said firmly, and curled my lip for the benefit of the rich people around me eating proper steaks. "It's nothing but hamburger."

Nobody seemed to hear and I knew I was overpowered and would suffer the scorn of the whole family. But this time something happened that well might have influenced my grasshopper life. Specialists in child discipline warn us that punishment must be swift and sure and appropriate lest good and evil be forever confused. But here came the Negro again with sizzling plates, each with a charming silver cap, and when we lifted these lids every single one of us beheld not hamburger and onions, but a steak complete with delectable golden circles of French-fried onions and a touch of parsley that rendered the whole beyond any Thanksgiving plate I had ever seen.

Dad looked up angrily. "I ordered *ground* steak!" he said.

But the Negro was smiling and nodding and the steward hurried over, smiling and nodding too. He had ordered the steaks himself, he said. With his compliments, then—

A wonder my chin did not crack, going up. I saw my brother and my sisters looking with helpless rapture at their plates. Afterward, there were salads served each on its own plate, ice cream sprinkled with nuts and swimming in caramel, and then green and white mints served so generously that one could slip some into a pocket without being noticed. Dad and Mother drank coffee in tiny flowered cups, and we wove back through the cars in beautiful family accord. My sin was never mentioned again.

By dawn I could concede the Royal Gorge its depth, the canyons their wonder, and Denver was mine to the limit of its gold-leafed dome. I was smitten forever by the joy of travel. When the same Negro porter presided over our return to Utah, I could ask no more.

It was only a few weeks after our great journey that I saw another Negro, but this time, of all unlikely places, he was sitting in the church when I went to Sunday school. There he was, as still as a statue, looking very dignified and neat in dark go-to-meeting clothes. He was alone in the back row; I turned my head as I passed, and he smiled.

"Hello!" I was surprised at my own voice.

"Hello!" His voice came back unexpectedly big.

Carol was saving a seat for me, as always. Our class had to sit together during preliminary exercises, so we could be watched by our teachers and marched promptly to the classroom below. Nudging me, Carol whispered, "You talked to that nigger!"

"Ya—ya, I did." I looked back. Through the bustle of arrivals I perceived his isolation. The bench stretched empty on either side. "I wish I could go back and sit by him," I said with sudden feeling.

"You *do?*" Carol spoke admiringly, as she did for any daring thing I might say or do. It was for her I had learned to stand on my head and turn a cartwheel three times in a row.

"He's just sitting there all alone. Why doesn't *some-body—*"

"Father talked to him when he came in. He's just going through town on his way to California. He knew Mark Petersen down in Tennessee." Carol always knew things, because her father was Bishop of our Ward. He stood at the door and spoke to everybody who came to church, shaking hands and talking and making everything nice as if Sunday School were a big party and he the host. One of his two Councilors always stood at the other door.

"Did Mark give him the Gospel?" I asked with admiration. Mark was on a mission to the Deep South; I had been to his Farewell and had heard his prayerful resolve to help convert the world to the Plan of Salvation. Suddenly I remembered something I had learned in Religion Class. "Maybe he wants to come to Utah and join the Church and get to be 'white and delightsome!' "

That was a quotation any Mormon understood. But I had it wrong, Carol instantly informed me. "That's not for niggers," she said. "That's just for Indians."

The organ had begun to play and Carol's father stood up at the rostrum and our teacher looked at us warningly and said, "Sssssh!"

Not for Negroes; only for Indians. As the singing began, I turned it over in my mind. I'd have to ask; Carol must be wrong. Anyhow, to be white was not, in my opinion, to be particularly delightsome. I envied the Indians up at the Fort Duchesne reservation their glorious bronze, and every spring tried to convert my pasty winter white into something like it, only to bloom with a hideous splotch of freckles. Now I thought of the face of my friend on the magic train, his white teeth and his full happy lips and his wonderful hands so deftly handing out silver and smoking steak. Certainly he was delightsome already. God would never have made such a foolish mistake.

The first song began, rather straggly, as first songs tend to be, and suddenly we all knew that something splendid had come to swell our devotions. A big bass voice boomed out from the back bench. Brother Johnson, the chorister who was also principal of the high school, smiled and looked back there over his waving stick. It was a good feeling, Brother Johnson and the Negro smiling at each other with their voices meeting over all of the other voices and the organ too. Brother Johnson had the biggest voice in our town and there was never a program or an opera or a funeral or a wedding without him in charge. His wife played the organ, and now she too looked back and smiled to hear the Negro's voice. People turned to stare.

The service went on. Scripture Reading. The Three-Minute Talk by a small boy who told in a singsong voice about the vision of Joseph Smith. The practice song was the best I had ever heard, with the bass swelling out as never before. When Brother Johnson had the sopranos alone, the altos, the tenors, I waited breathlessly for the basses. A good feeling swept the audience, because the Negro knew his part so well. "Now *everybody!*"

How we sang!

To this day, whenever I go to a church that has perfunctory hymns from the book without community practice, I miss Mormon singing. Community choirs in Utah become excellent through sheer delight, as bell ringers do in English villages. Grass-roots excellence eventually leads to the Tabernacle Choir. At the height of organ music stands the Tabernacle Organ, its luster spread over all the world. When Brother Johnson said, "Thank you—thank you very much!" we knew he meant to thank the smiling stranger in the back row. He had dark skin himself, Brother Johnson, for he farmed all summer, and his smile too was wide and white. "Choir practice at seven Wednesday!" he reminded the congregation. "Everybody come!"

Later, during Sacrament, I longed to turn around and see the Negro partake of the bread and the water. But I was beginning to despise all the rest of the people for staring. One little girl stood right up on the bench and looked and looked, and I knew uncomfortably how disconcerting a child's stare could be. What class would the Negro go to, I wondered, and it struck me that grownups either went to Church Doctrine or Genealogy. If the Negro went to Genealogy, where people learned how to search for their ancestors in order to be baptized by proxy for them in the Temple, it would be a queer thing. Genealogy classes were not intended for Negroes whose ancestors came on ships quite different from a well-documented Mayflower. I had seen neat family trees that went practically back to Adam, but even elementary history told me how many ancient African trees the great wind of slavery must have shaken to the roots.

Sister Johnson began a smart march, we stood up at a signal, and waited for our turn, facing the aisle. I saw the Negro rise and move out of the front door.

Our class buzzed with talk. Somebody said the Negro was camped with his wife and two small boys out by Petersen's farm, south of town. Mark Petersen, on a mission in the South, had met them when they were fishing down in Tennessee, and being a fisherman himself had fallen into talk about Utah and what he claimed was "the best fishing for the best fish in the world." He had written to his folks later that they could expect a visitor for a few days, and had asked them to find a place for a truck and tent.

"I saw him coming out of the canyon—he had a whole string," one of the boys said. "He gave the Petersens a mess for breakfast." He laughed. "And do you know what he *said?* He said trout was '*almost as good as cat*'!"

I was outraged by the unfair laughter. "Cat*fish*, you know, cat*fish*!" I cried. But "cat" was repeated over and over during the next few days, as if he were a monster from whom even our pets were not safe.

On the way home I said to Carol, "I wonder if Mark gave him the Gospel? That's for *everybody*."

Even about this she had her doubts. "Missionaries don't preach to niggers," she said.

"Don't say 'nigger.' It's not nice," I said. "When we went to Denver, Mother told me it wasn't nice."

"Why?" she asked.

I didn't know. Just because. But suddenly I realized how very much I didn't know. A black skin had something to do with a quarrel between Christ and his brother, Lucifer, before the world began. Vaguely I realized what it was about—Free Agency, the right to choose between good and evil. Almost every day of my life I was choosing, like that day on the dining car, and many other days, with problems far more serious. It made me uncomfortable to think of Jesus arguing just like anybody else, right before God His Father, who could surely have settled the matter, if he wished, without much trouble. But that was how we got our glorious Plan of Salvation, for which people were thankful in Testimony Meeting on the first Sunday of every month. It was a shame that Lucifer had to stay so upset about being beaten, I thought, knocking around the world ever since, at loose ends and with too much time on his hands. But of course it was something to upset anybody, his brother coming down and getting all of the glory.

"Isn't there something about the curse of Ham?" I asked,

for I dimly recalled something in the Book of Abraham about blackness being a result of the "sons of Cain" refusing to repent.

"Anybody knows about that," Carol said. "Niggers can get baptized but they can't get the Priesthood."

"Why?" I asked.

But that she did not know and I carried the question home to dinner. My father looked bothered and said, "Why don't you ask Carol's father? He's the Bishop."

But when Carol and I approached her father, later in the day, he looked bothered too. "Of course Negroes will have the Priesthood in the fullness of time," he said. "That's promised. But who are *we*—" He frowned at us and retreated behind his *Deseret News*. "Who are we to question God and the Prophet?"

During the week we learned where the Negro was camped, and when we went out to Crystal Springs to swim we lingered by the fence to see whether his wife and sons might come out of the little tent pitched beside Petersen's meadow. The Petersens, we learned, had let the visitors pick apples and vegetables and gave them milk and eggs and cream. A few days later, Carol rushed to tell me that she had seen the Negro woman in the grocery store, and then had walked behind her and the little boys while they looked into windows on Main Street.

I hurried to town, but there was no sign. I longed to see the little black boys, one about eight, as lucky people said, and one "just a toddler, but black as the ace of spades." I persuaded Dad to take us riding past the Petersens' place when we went out in the evening, but no sign at all. Mother said I was silly to be so interested, that Negro children looked like anybody else. She was rather cross about it. In Religion Class that fall, when we asked our eternal Why, we were told that when Brigham Young came across the plains he brought two Negroes with him.

The driver of his best carriage for many years was one of these. "Joseph Smith was one of the greatest champions the Negro ever had," our teacher said, "and when he ran for President of the United States, he was more in favor of freedom than Abraham Lincoln himself." She explained that Joseph Smith had to run for President because no candidate promised to do anything for either Mormons or Negroes, two troubled peoples. "You should read his platform. He said that all slaves should be freed right away and their owners paid by the government. If anybody else had been as wise as that, maybe we wouldn't have had to fight the Civil War."

I was impressed. I still am, for I found that the teacher's account was substantially true.

For five weeks the tent stood in the same place. Every single Sunday the Negro sat in the same place in Sunday school, lending his voice to the singing. He held his book high in front of his face, his head proudly back, his mouth opening very wide to make his bigness free. Brother Johnson asked him to come to choir practice, and he came twice, much to the glory of God. Then he moved his family up the canyon, where they camped near the town reservoir. I recall how careful people were about letting their children go on hikes after that, for of course I eagerly sought to go. We had been free to hike where we pleased before that summer, but suddenly all mothers demanded that we have groups and chaperones. When our Sunday school class went on a picnic, we saw the little tent among the trees, pitched beside the Negro's shabby truck. But of the family we saw no sign that day.

It was beginning to be fall, a busy time. School started and all the track meets and games and class elections and organizing the orchestra and chorus and band and dozens of other things. The Church was activated too, after the relative quiet of summer. Now there was Primary and

Religion Class and Scouts and Beehive and Seagull Girls and Mutual Improvement Association. We were busy every moment of light, helping to harvest apples and pears and pumpkins, and sometimes in the evenings we raked leaves into piles and roasted apples and potatoes. Fragrant smoke drifted over the town, and the mountains swam in purple autumn haze.

One night Carol and I were eating potatoes by a dying fire, our fingers black with the burned skins. And suddenly I thought of the Negro. Was he still up there in the mountains? When we asked we learned that he had been seen by hunters, and had helped drag a buck around the reservoir. He had told Brother Petersen that he loved the mountains as he loved no other place in the world, and figured to stay until it got too cold. Warm days, cold nights. Plenty of fish. It had never been like that down in Tennessee.

Looking up at the glory of the hills, I understood how he must feel. As always, people said there had never been a more beautiful fall. Day after day there was a cloudless sky, and I could imagine how it was in the mountains high up where aspens made incredible golden carpets among the dark of pines. I liked to think of the Negro casting his line out into the colored lake. It was so clear, the still mountain water, that when one took a photograph it was hard to tell which was up and which was down.

On a night in early October our Mutual Improvement Association had its annual Autumn Dance, a pre-Halloween costume ball, with prizes, and Carol and I always dressed alike and went together, with dates or without. This time, perhaps thinking of the Negro, she suggested that we black our faces and go dressed as minstrels. Her father had played End Man at the Oddfellows' Show, and she knew how to make black with soot from under the stove lids and a little cold cream.

But I said no, hardly understanding my own revulsion. "It's not funny at all," I said. "That silly jigging. And those big red lips—" So we refurbished some Dutch costumes we had worn in a school show the year before, and found some real wooden shoes that had come home with a missionary from Denmark. Clomping around the hall, we had a wild good time. It was fun to watch people coming in and dancing around, guessing who they were behind their masks, and making our own lists of First, Second, Third Prize.

We were trying to dance, I remember, when The Ghost arrived. It was swathed in shining white from head to foot, with white gloves and white shoes and everything. When it floated through the door alone, we were not even sure whether it was man or woman. There were almost no eyes cut in the hood, only the merest slits through which one caught a glimpse of eye-shine now and then. Right away it approached the prettiest girl in the hall, who was dressed as a gypsy, and took her wildly around the floor, the white sheet billowing behind.

"That's the best costume—that's First," I said.

Carol agreed.

We were resting our poor, clomping feet near the bandstand when we heard a woman say, "It's that Negro. I'll bet anything it's him."

It was the costume itself that suggested him, I see now. It was a terrible costume, actually, was it not, the one in which we had heard people did unmentionable things to the poor colored people of the South?

"Imagine—*dancing with all the girls—*"

Such consternation, growing like a wildfire, I have never seen. Swiftly a group gathered. Members of the Dance Committee were brought one by one from the floor. And then and there, they held a meeting. We watched them, talking and looking and gesticulating, moving off to the privacy of the kitchen behind the refreshment stand.

"What difference does it make if he dances with the girls?" I demanded. "Why, he has *gloves* on!"

But we both sensed the strength of feeling among the determined band of officers when they filed back out of the kitchen and around the dance floor to speak to the leader of the band. The drum rolled and the president of the Mutual Improvement Association stood up to make an announcement. The dancing stopped. People came crowding forward to hear.

"Brothers and Sisters . . ." We would unmask now and the prizes would be distributed; it had been decided not to wait until intermission.

There was a degree of fairness; a gesture had been made. "First Prize—to The Ghost!"

There was a patter of applause as he came forward. Everybody had begun to laugh and tug at the ribbons of their masks, and he lifted his white gloves to remove the hood. Every eye in the room was fastened on him.

It was Brother Johnson, good Brother Johnson, waving and laughing and climbing onto the stand to claim his own.

The Negro had not come at all.

We danced until "Home Sweet Home," and I remember walking with our crowd through the crisp autumn night. Nobody said a word about the Negro that night or afterward, and he was never seen in our town again. But I never went into Sunday school without feeling his presence, a white ghost, in the back row.

The Other Lady

Actually I saw her on only two occasions. Yet they were both so dramatic that she seems to figure larger in my childhood than some of the people I knew well for years. I have been told that she was rather ordinary, and that may be. I only know she was not ordinary when I saw her, either time. The first time, of course, she was in love, and therefore transfigured. The other time she was totally bereft. The dates, April and November of the same year, are entirely too symbolic, but this I cannot help. I invent the time still less than the emotion.

That a young woman should be in love with my tall handsome grandfather, then in his late fifties, seemed perfectly natural to me from the beginning. But that my grandmother should be upset I was fascinated to hear, because she was not the sort of person who ever got upset. She was so square and firm and impassive that one kissed her when she came for a visit as one might kiss a wall. One did not think of her as a wall that protected or obscured, or even as a barrier, for she refused her grandchildren nothing. One did not think particularly, either, of the words "strong" and "good," though both were true. She was simply *there*, like the house in which one has been born and in which one therefore habitually lives. There is a story about how effortlessly she bore her babies, dropping them by the way like an Indian. When I overheard my parents saying that she had gone to bed and lay biting her nails to the quick because of a certain letter she had found in Grandfather's traveling coat, I could scarcely imagine it. But I was so interested that the vision of it would not leave my mind.

Grandfather had traveled as far back as I could remember. Once he had managed a big store of his own, but in some great depression—"the Cleveland depression" I think it was—his store had been lost. So his undeniable salesmanship talents were sold to the Mormon Church, whose great Zion's Cooperative Mercantile Institution still bears the sign of the watchful Eye of God. Every few weeks his travels brought him to our valley, several hundred miles south of Salt Lake City, and the evenings he spent with us were like towering peaks over the gentle sunny plains of our village life. He was over six feet tall, an expansive Dane, and kissing him was an experience big and complete. He opened his arms and you entered an enchanted masculine warmth; he had the smooth clean feel of a fine gentleman. Best of all, his embrace was never overdone. Almost instantly he held you off and looked at you, and then the wonder was his voice and his laugh. "And since last time," he would say, "how has it been?"

It was usually on Friday that he came, completing his circuit for the weekend, and sometimes he met us when we came from the Friday afternoon matinee. I was so proud to walk on Main Street beside him that I still feel the stretch of my lifted chin when I think of it. His black suit, his gloves, his hat, his immaculate shirt front and tie, his glossy shoes—among the farmers of our community he was a shining light, and it could be they resented him,

I do not know. He even carried a fine stick, like a man on a stage, but this went under his arm when he held my hand and my sister's hand, one on either side. He had acted for a time in the Salt Lake Theater, and certainly his voice was theatrically rich. He had to know everything that had happened to us, about our marks at school, about the Primary Show we had appeared in, the new songs we had learned. Invariably something we had accomplished must have a reward, and the reward was always a new silver dollar. *New* is the important thing: Grandfather's Dollars were always fresh from the mint. No money ever made can have felt or looked so much like *money* as those great round Western dollars he gave to us. To this day I still feel, when I happen to see one, that it must be worth a dozen dollar bills. We saved our Grandfather Dollars, laying them carefully upon tinted cotton in pretty boxes as if they were jewels.

It was a week before Easter that I overheard the news about Grandmother. She had been expected to visit us during the spring holidays. It was after supper and Dad sat frowning over a letter from one of his sisters. "Why, it's ridiculous," he said. "Father never had anything to do with another woman. Somebody with a hat shop, over in Ephraim. Have you ever heard of her?"

"Only that she makes pretty hats," Mother said.

Something about the way she said it made Dad angry right away. "Well, I won't have you trotting over there to find out!" he said.

"Why not?" Mother asked, looking lively.

"Because I don't believe a word of it. Women—" He looked at the letter again. "They imagine things."

"If it's not true, why shouldn't I go?" Mother asked. "A good many women here get their Easter hats from her. They say she studied millinery in the East."

Dad said No, absolutely No, forever No. But the very next afternoon, which was a Saturday, we left as soon as he had gone back to work after noon. We were back in plenty of time for Mother to get supper.

It is odd to remember how far seven miles seemed in those days. When I go back to Utah now, those two little towns seem almost one to me, they are so close together. The houses, too, that I always thought spacious and elegant are really quite small and commonplace. How shall one be sure of anything at all then? But they say a vision is partly the eye that perceives it, as the ear must record the falling of a tree. That day I fell in love with the most beautiful pink bonnet ever made, and it is no wonder that I have remembered its creator, there in her charming little shop, as a woman of surpassing loveliness and generosity.

Before we arrived I was set for drama.

Mother said to us, energetically steering as she spoke (for she always drove as if the car must be made to go by her own force), "We're going for *hats*, you understand? I don't want either of you letting on we came to see *her*."

Helen, almost two years my senior, looked sidewise at me, and I thought she meant to enforce Mother's words, so I made a face at her. But presently she said to Mother, "Well, anyway, we *do* get hats, don't we?"

"Of course we get hats! That's what I told you we were going for."

"But if we take hats home, Dad will know where we went."

The car lurched. Mother deliberately drove it off the road and stopped. Immediately, as always when Mother stopped the car, the engine died. She turned to us, but with her gloved hands still clutching the wheel. "Naturally I meant to tell your father the minute we got home." Her voice was severe. "*I'll* tell him," she said, looking at me, for I was always the one to spill everything at the wrong time.

"I only thought—" Helen began, and stopped suddenly, staring ahead.

"*What* did you think?" Mother asked. "Honestly, you'd think your father and I could talk about something, just ourselves, just once in a while!" She looked at us with a kind of hopeless anger. "If I catch either of you repeating one word of this outside of the family, I'll spank you good. Do you hear? I shouldn't have brought you."

My eyes were on my sister's face, which was turning redder and redder. She knew something I did not; I could tell it. And I had believed she told me everything. She and I had agreed that we could speak of anything together —even of things Mother called "nasty" and would not speak about any more than she would breathe a word of scandal. It was a good joke between us how Mother would *not* notice a mess even when she was physically involved in cleaning it up. This, I think, was part of her Englishness; with the English, I've noticed since, nobody cares whether a thing is *done*, just so it is not mentioned.

But Mother was noticing Helen's face. "Did you read that letter?" she demanded. "If you did—"

"No. No, I didn't! I didn't even see any letter," Helen said, but her eyes looked set, suddenly, as if she fought to hold her tears.

"Then what was it you thought?"

"Nothing. I didn't think anything."

"You did. I can tell you did." Mother's voice sharpened. "Has anybody been *saying* anything?" she asked in despair.

"No. It was only that I—" Helen paused one long second and then plunged. "It was just that I saw Grandfather. Last week when I went over with Mr. Reid, when he brought the books over." Mr. Reid was the County Superintendent of Schools, a kindly man who sometimes let his daughters and their friends go along, up and down the county, on errands he had to make.

"You saw him! You couldn't— He wasn't even down last week," Mother said.

I must confess that I enjoyed the look on her face. Overcome as I was that Helen had not told me, I was fascinated and full of admiration as well that she had not told Mother. Imagine keeping such a thing to yourself! I could no more have done that than I could have stopped breathing. Mother seemed to hang onto the wheel; Helen wept into her hands. At last Mother's voice came again, hollowly. "Was he with *her?*"

"He was there by her store. They were laughing and talking."

"On the street? Right there on Main Street?" Mother cried.

"She was on the step, holding the door open."

"Was he—could you tell? Was he going in?" She paused terribly. "Or coming out?"

"I don't know. We went on by, and nobody saw him but me. When we came back they weren't there."

Mother leaned forward on the wheel, rubbing her forehead back and forth. "Why didn't you tell us?" she asked. "You should have come right home and told us."

Helen turned her eyes to me then, and I'm sure mine were asking accusingly, Why didn't you tell *me?* She could have told me, whether or not she was able to tell Mother. "I thought he'd come for supper," she said miserably. "I thought maybe he wanted it to be a surprise."

"But when he didn't come? And when we got that letter—"

"I didn't think about it. I don't know—" She was really saying she didn't want it to be true.

We sat in silence. Then Mother lifted her head again,

decisively. "Well!" she said. "Well, then! I think it's high time we came over!" The car roared and went lurching onto the road again; Mother did not glance behind her, for after all nothing much except hayracks ever came along that road. In two minutes we came to a stop every bit as decisive as the start, exactly in front of the little shop, by a rusted hitching post. A sign said "Hat Shoppe" in elegant black letters over a window filled with the very breath of a feminine spring.

Mother looked at the place and then at herself in the little mirror at the side of the car. Firmly she removed her old winter hat and laid it on the back seat. "Well, come on!" she said.

I expected from the look on her face that she meant to march right in and start shouting something important, maybe the Ten Commandments. But she paused at the window. She looked carefully at the hats, each on a little white pedestal wound with ribbons. I spun, agitated as a top, on the step, wanting whatever it was going to be to happen now, at once, but Mother leaned to the glass, intent as if searching for a clue.

"The straws are pretty," she said in her most ordinary shopping voice.

But then I saw the pink hat. And for a time I saw nothing else, nothing in the window or in the street or in the entire universe. That spring, for a change, it was fashionable again even for grown women to be fussy and feminine. For little girls a kind of poke-bonnet was the rage, and this was such a bonnet—but more, much much more. It had that certain indefinable quality that only a few hats have in this world, a peculiar saucy excitement in its very shape, not too decorative, but only *so*— One fancied one's face deep within, rosy and mysterious with the freckles mercifully hidden. Frankly sentimental, the hat was made of rows of pink satin ribbon that were all one piece, even the two lengths to tie, turning upon themselves, with every stitch invisible. Mother too has always remembered it. Two very blue forget-me-nots with tiny yellow centers sat at the very edge of the crown, their stems tucked in. At the foot of the pedestal lay a small blue bouquet upon a frail flower of pink handkerchief.

"Oh, *Mother* . . ." I could scarcely breathe. I was already seeing myself as I came into Sunday School, my eyes watchful from their deep pink place, the pink handkerchief in my hand, the flowers pinned to my collar, against my throat. "Mother, can I try it on? Can I? Can I?"

"There's no price on it. We'll see. It's probably too expensive," Mother said.

"I think it's babyish," said Helen.

"Babyish? Just because it's pink and blue?" I cried out as if she had taken the Lord's name in vain.

"Well, I like plain straw," she said. She was trying to please Mother; I did not even glance at the hat she pointed out.

Mother nodded. "I'd really thought of straw," she said. And I clutched at her then, saying, "Oh, Mother . . ." the way I'd learned to do long since. "I'll put all my allowance—"

"You've 'put' all your allowance on ten different things already and you know it," she said firmly. "Please don't be silly just now. Especially not just now." She turned toward the step and opened the door.

So it was I entered the Shoppe in a daze of selfish concern, a thousand times less interested in the other lady herself than in her proprietorship of the fabulous pink hat. She was sewing when we came in, sitting at a machine in one corner of the little room, surrounded with the makings of her bonnets. Spools of ribbons stood on a shelf behind her, the colors shaded light to dark, like a rainbow. There were cards of lace, piles of flowers and handkerchiefs, an array of colored feathers. There were shapes for hats of various kinds, some of straw and some of stiff white tape. I noted much of this right away, with the sort of ardent concern with which one views the house where his love was born.

I remember how tall and thin she looked when she rose, perhaps because I had been thinking of her in terms of Grandmother, who was short and very plump. Her cheeks went red and she lifted her hands at once to push her hair from her forehead, as a woman will do when a man enters a room unexpectedly. She knew us. She spoke to Mother at once by her name.

As I recall it, Mother was the more flustered of the two. She said at once that we had come to look at hats, to my horror adding, "I'd thought of simple straws for the girls—little sailors, I think. There's one in the window."

"Mother—" I sought her hand. "The pink one—ask if I can try on the pink one—"

The lady looked at me. She smiled. "It's very pretty, isn't it?" she said. "I just finished it this morning."

"I'm really not interested in anything that dressy," Mother said hastily. "Something simple—a little shade, their faces burn so all summer."

I knew she meant that my hat was too expensive, and suddenly, acknowledging the truth of what she had said of my allowance, and also, I imagine, inspired by the present drama, I cried out: "Mother, I'll pay all of my Grandfather Dollars, every single one!"

Mother gave me a terrible look. Helen gave me a terrible pinch. But I did not mind either one, for the lady proceeded at once to the window and lifted up not only the obnoxious straw but the pink hat as well, spinning a bit on its cunning pedestal. "There," she said, setting it down in front of the mirror by the wall. "A pretty girl like you should have a pretty hat."

I would have given my life for her on the spot. She could have done anything and I would have forgiven her. At that moment I truly believe she could have tied up my handsome and beloved grandfather in a gunny sack and carried him off to the North Pole and I would not have offended her by objecting. Even my bosom friend, in her wildest adoration, had never gone so far as to suggest that I was pretty. How I really looked in the hat I have no idea, but it was a creation that even enhanced its pedestal, so it might have enhanced me. The lady drew it over my head and expertly tied the ribbons into an enchanting bow under my left ear. I stood gazing into the glass.

Mother stood still. Helen gave a nervous giggle. Then, with a determined look, Mother reached over and looked at the price tag which was apparently hanging at the back of my neck. I saw her do it, in the glass.

"I promise, I'll give *all*—" I began again.

It was the lady herself who interrupted. "You must let me give it to her," she said to Mother. Her face was scarlet but Mother looked quite pale. With those words our whole errand, the whole truth, was laid instantly bare.

"Why, I wouldn't think of such a thing!" Mother said.

"I'd be so glad if you would," the lady said, and leaned on her shaking fingers on a table laden with hats. "If we could be friends—all of us—" Then, shockingly, she used my grandfather's given name. "He'd be so pleased," she said.

Without another word, Mother turned and left the shop. Helen stumbled after. And there I stood, crowned in my rosy splendor, not knowing what to do.

"Please take it," the lady said.

But of course I could not. I could never wear such a creation home, or explain it. I lifted a heavy hand and slipped the bow undone. I'm sure no ballad bridegroom was ever torn from his bride with more anguish than I felt as I slipped that hat from my head and laid it reverently down. Mother was starting the car. When I heard the engine roaring, I flew in a panic to the door. One second I paused there, saying, "It's the prettiest hat in the world!" and the door slammed after me.

"Get in!" Mother said.

All the way home she blamed herself and me, turn and turn about. Dad always knew best, she said, why hadn't she remembered that? And I—I had spoiled everything with that silly pink hat, talking about Grandfather. But before we came into our street we decided, like conspirators, that since we had no hats to explain we needn't confess our escapade, after all. We stopped at Brown's for ice-cream sundaes and then went to our own hat shop where we thought quite simply about hats and bought two for shade. I can't say I was entirely reconciled about the pink one, either that day or for many days thereafter. I only say it was one of many lessons in that same sort of resignation and that I would have done without them all if I could.

It must have been the following week that Grandfather was waiting for us after the Friday matinee. He was standing behind the little copper rail in front of the ticket window, watching the stream of children come out. We were always dazed, coming into the blast of level afternoon light from the flickering dark. Grandfather looked unreal for a while, as the whole world did. But his hand was reassuring, and his strong hug. I thought, "So he still loves us; he still comes to see us too," and felt wildly happy as we walked along Main Street. Yet when we turned at our corner and he asked, familiarly, "And how has it been since last time?" there was a long moment when we could not think what to say. He spoke again himself before either of us could answer, his voice as usual, teasing and gay. "I hear you offered all your silver dollars for a bonnet."

Suddenly, dreadfully, Helen broke from his hand and began to run. When we came to our gate, in the first deep silence I had ever known with my grandfather, she had disappeared. I looked up at his face as he carefully fastened the gate after us, and for the first time in my life felt the sorrow of being beside a person I loved and yet helplessly apart. For a moment his face sagged, deep lines gathered above his white collar. And then he pushed out his lower lip and his chin came up in a way that was particularly his; he took my hand again and we walked around the path which curved against the lawn. As we climbed the steps to the porch, the front door opened and Dad came out.

He spoke to me, holding the door wide. "Go in," he said. I went in and the door closed after me. Instantly I was at the window looking onto the porch, filled with terror. Wasn't Grandfather to come in to supper, to laugh, to talk, to tell all the wonderful comical things that had happened since the last time? I suppose I knew. It seems to me I knew what was said between them, every syllable, though it isn't possible that I really heard. I knew from their mouths, their gestures. Grandfather held out his hand and it simply stood there, on the air.

Then Grandfather's hand fell at his side and he turned and went down the steps and around the path and through the gate and down the street, out of sight. None of us ever saw him alive again.

The news of his death came from California the next November. The divorce had happened quickly, in Nevada, and he was married again at once. But one day, not long afterward, he was cranking a car and fell, so we were told, and died in the street. He was brought back to Utah to be buried in the family plot.

I remember the feeling of importance amidst my sorrow; I was to stay out of school and to travel on the train. The fact of death was impossible to believe, especially about Grandfather, and so I did not really believe it until I saw it. I looked into the coffin only once, and it was a long time before the vision of Grandfather in his black suit and fine tie and gloves and hat and stick overcame again the dreadful unnatural vision of him lying in pure white with his eyes closed and his shoes sticking oddly up into the air. There was a curious cap on his head and his hands were folded over an apron of bright green, embroidered with patterns of leaves, the Mormon burial clothes. All afternoon everybody kept kissing everybody, which was to me a difficult trial. I remember my turn coming with each aunt and uncle, each distant cousin, and with poor Grandmother it was worst of all for she tasted of salt and trembled, another creature than the hearty woman I had always known, almost as different as Grandfather himself.

It was from the midst of the family kissing that I first saw the other lady. She stood against the wall, beside the door, completely alone. If anybody spoke to her or looked at her, I did not see it. As for kissing, of course that was out of the question, one advantage at least of her position. After that, from deep among the scores of cousins and second cousins and third cousins, I kept seeking her out, and have no idea whether my fascination was only curiosity or whether I felt pity too. The pity may have come later; how can one be sure? I only know that I see her now as unmistakably as I see Grandfather, in slim black, unrelieved from top to toe by any ornament, or by even so much as the shine of a button. At the funeral she followed behind the family, far behind Grandmother and her long procession of tall sons and daughters, her grandchildren, her brothers and sisters, nephews and nieces. The lady came down the aisle, walking alone; I saw from my important place on the end of the front row that there was now one spot of pure white upon her, a handkerchief she held in her right hand.

Later I saw her at the graveside. It was then she caught my eye, once, but I quickly looked at the ground again. She was wearing a very tight and very ugly black hat, and none of her hair was showing. She who had so many pretty hats. It was certain, then, that she no longer cared for hats or for anything.

Dad had to return home that night, for there was nobody to relieve him at his work next morning. We left for the train soon after the fabulous dinner that followed the funeral. When we came to the depot, the other lady was there, sitting in the waiting room, alone on a long straight-backed bench. I will never forget Mother in the next moment. She stood for a time like a person about to jump into the sea, her face streaked and her hat awry. And then she rushed suddenly over to the other lady and sat down and they cried together. Dad said nothing. He made no sign of recognition, then or later, on the train. I knew he was remembering, as I was, the last time Grandfather had come to our house, holding out his hand.

The lady sat alone on the train, far down the aisle on the other side. The train was overheated and soot drifted along the sills of the windows. The conductor turned the lights out, except for a small one at either end of the car, and everybody slept. Once in a while the train stopped, people moved a little, murmuring together, and slept again. I remember waking for the last time looking up half-stupefied at Mother standing over me. Beside her was the other lady, with a little satchel and the ugly black hat in her hand. Her hair was tumbled and her face flushed. "I would so like to kiss her, if I may," she said.

Mother said, "Of course."

The lady leaned down over me and I felt the brief warm pressure of her lips. She smelled of something sweet, barely spiced, and a great flood of excited love came over me. I moved close. The train was stopping; she walked hurriedly down the aisle. I could hear Dad talking with the conductor in the vestibule, and turned to press my face against the window. I saw her walk alone across the lighted platform and then, presently, as the train started once again, she disappeared from sight.

The Face

Dad said kindly, "Now, honey, we'll forget all about it."

I did not yet know about forgetting. I only knew that even with the kitchen bright with sun, the door wide to the flowering dooryard, I was still in that other hour. Dad had brought in another bushel of peaches for bottling, and their smell and fuzz filled the air and flies buzzed desperately at the screens. I sat safely at the table in the center of the room and Mother dropped sections of cut peach on my corn flakes. They lay ripe and yellow, each piece with a touch of coxcomb red where the seed had lain.

"Peach fuzz hurts my nose," I said, because my eyes had filled with tears and my nose was truly stinging. I sneezed. Three times in a row. They all looked at me, and Mother laughed and said, "God bless you, God bless you, God bless you!"

"She wants to get out of peeling," Dad said, rather crossly, because my tears bothered him. He always got cross with us when we cried and it was years before I understood this was because our tears gave him an unmanly need to cry too.

"Peeling isn't fuzzy," Mother said. "I'll scald them first."

"It's just nerves making her sneeze anyway," Dad said. "She always sneezes or gets bellyache when she's nervous, doesn't she?"

"Ssssh," Mother said, and talked of something else.

I sat turning my spoon among the fruit and flakes, not seeing anything really except the face I remembered, or tried to remember. But nothing certain would come to me, only that it was round and very white. The eyes had been nothing but two shinings, like a cat's eyes caught in the headlights of a car. Yet I had a feeling it was a face I knew, one I had seen before. Searching my mind to give it a name was terrible, frightening. Every waking moment since I saw it I had been struggling to fasten it down somehow, and I would come to the very edge of knowing and then it would vanish once more. For the briefest, longest, most shattering second I had seen it, over the first ledge of the bathroom window, high up, so I had to lift my own face to look. Dad had painted only the lower half of the window, because the other half was so high nobody could ever see in. It was so high that the one with the round face had to remove (how quietly) the bottles from an old table Mother had set at the head of the dirt cellar, by the flat cellar door, before he was high enough. Carefully he had laid the bottles in a row, on the ground under the table, setting them apart so they would not tinkle. I had heard Dad speak about this to the night watchman when he came. How carefully and how deliberately this must have been done. "You can't imagine such a thing. It must have been a maniac," Dad said.

Maniac meant somebody quite mad, I knew. Like Mr. Elder, who lived out over the creek. But he was dead now. It had been strange to see a quiet old man like Mr. Elder doing such peculiar things. When his wife died, just before the funeral when everybody was going to see

him and taking him things and sympathizing—the whole
Relief Society was there, preparing a lunch for the mourners, people said—and he suddenly became somebody else.
Before, his face had been compressed into a strong knot
of weeping and seemed naturally changed in sorrow, a
natural funeral face. But suddenly he began to shout, and
his eyes went wide and active in their sockets, burning
terribly, and he threw his arms about, crying, "*I was cruel,
you all know it, she knew it, I was cruel, cruel!*" His
friends had to hold him. And after a time he was quiet,
like himself again. But after that he always walked with
his eyes on the ground. And then one day they found him
lying in the creek, swollen and blue.

But I couldn't imagine a man like Mr. Elder moving
the bottles so carefully. He would have swept them off,
they would have smashed, he would have run away. There
must be different kinds of maniacs, then. The neighborhood men and the night watchman had searched the
ground, trying with flashlights and lanterns to find foot-
prints; but the ground was dry, there hadn't been a rain
for several weeks. The night watchman, whom I had
seen sometimes trying doors along Main Street after a
picture show, carrying a great ring of keys, or moving
around the park on band-concert nights warning young
people to be quiet during the solos, had come into the
kitchen, asking questions.

Did the face remind me of anybody?

"No," I said uncertainly, "it was round and white with
shining eyes."

"*That* helps," my brother Claude said in disgust.

Mother finally said, "Don't ask her any more about it,"
because I had begun to shiver uncontrollably. She wrapped
me in a warm blanket and put my feet on the open oven
door and gave me a cup of hot milk.

At the door, the watchman turned and said, "I haven't

heard of a Peeping Tom in this town for years." He had a
pale and serious face, and stood, lingering, his hat in his
hand.

Dad said again, "It must have been a maniac."

"We're short on maniacs lately," the watchman said,
and laughed in a short and ugly way. "I kind of wish I
had one, if you know what I mean. The thing is, there's
nothing to go on. Except that whoever it was seemed to
know the place."

He was looking at me. His face was familiar, yet I had
never really looked at it before. He was always moving
in the doorways, half in shadow, or on the outskirts of the
crowd. He had to be very good and very honest, I knew,
having keys to everything. A dishonest watchman could
just go in and take everything he liked, couldn't he, and
then pretend to look for thieves.

I shrank into the blanket and sipped my steaming milk.
Dad talked with him in the yard for a few minutes more
and Mother went out, too, and I knew they were looking
at the table and the bottles and everything again. Claude
said, probably because I was shivering over the steaming
milk, keeping the blanket high around my neck like an
Indian, "You were only looked at. You weren't *hurt*."

Finally I had been put to bed but the light was left
burning on my table and the blinds were down to the
sills in spite of the heat. It had been such a still night. I
had lain for a long time listening to the stillness. And now
it was day again; I had been glad to see the dawn.

"You're not eating," Mother said. "More sugar?"

"Yes, please," I said. Like a little girl, I let her sprinkle it,
and the yellow and red of the peaches became crystalline,
sucking the sweetness in. Then cream. I watched the
flakes and fruit become smothered, disappear. It was my
favorite dish, next to red raspberries. But I had no wish to
eat. My throat felt dry and thick. Dad looked at Mother,

I felt their looking over my bent head, and I knew how
Mother frowned a warning. No extra fuss, please. This
morning nothing should be said or insisted on or mentioned; they should act as if nothing unusual had happened. I picked among the peaches with the point of my
spoon, lifting the thin red threads of the coxcombs and
laying them apart.

"For heaven's sakes, don't pick like that. They're not
oysters," Dad said at last in a nervous voice. Once I had
been sick over a plate of raw oysters offered me on a holiday by the sea.

I did not look up, but I wanted to try, I really wanted
to help them. So I lifted a slice of peach carefully in my
spoon and put it into my mouth and chewed at it slowly.
It felt sturdy, like meat, but presently slipped down my
throat without trouble and I lifted another one. At the
front door Dad kissed Mother good-by and whispered
something about keeping me busy.

Whenever anybody was worried over something or had
troubles, Dad told them to work and work.

"Well, we've plenty to do today," Mother said heartily.
"Phyllis is coming to help too." Phyllis was her best friend
and they had their own little *kaffeeklatsch* almost every
day, first at one house and then the other. "Two's not
much of a brood of hens," Phyllis would say, "but if anybody else came, I swear I don't see how they'd get a word
in edgewise." They told each other everything, I knew.
They made quilts and jam and chili sauce and doilies and
did baskets of darning and mending. Nobody could say
they ever wasted any time.

I cleared the table and washed the dishes and dried them
and put them away. Mother put a large kettle on the stove
and got it to boiling. Into this she plunged a little basket
which held six big peaches at a time; this loosened the
skins and took the fuzz away. Then she ran cold water

over them and put them into a pan of water, on my lap. It was easy to peel them and the halves fell apart. I turned them properly downward in the bottles, the way Mother liked them, using a tablespoon in the bottle to slide them down and to turn them over if they fell with open sides up. All face down they fitted snugly, the bottles were much fuller, and they looked deliberately beautiful. All the First Prize fruit at the County Fair was done like that.

Mother kept chattering and counting and once in a while she went outside for more bottles to scald and get ready. Yesterday she had gone back and forth, up and down cellar, and had set up that old table for the bottles to save time today, to be ready for work this morning. Now she had only to go as far as the table—I saw her once, standing still with her arms full of bottles, looking up. Figuring, the way Dad and the watchman had, how it had been done. Carefully. Not something just like a flip of your finger, like for instance telling a quick lie because you're in a tight spot, or like hitting somebody who suddenly makes you angry, as my brother did now and then. This was what people called malice aforethought. Planned. I began to shiver again in the bright kitchen heat.

The bell rang sharply at the front door and I jumped, my hands lifted quickly against my chest. The water in the pan on my lap rocked into waves and spilled over onto my apron; I felt it running down my legs.

Mother hurried in. "That's probably Phyllis. I don't know *why* she can't come around to the back door, but she *never*—"

How they'd hold forth this morning when Mother had told her, I thought.

Phyllis had her waterproof apron on, and as usual she had her hands in her pockets and her arms akimbo. An easy woman, kind and real, like a sister, Mother always said of her. Now she looked at me kindly. "I'll swear, every time I see that girl she's a shade prettier. I tell your Mother, I never saw a girl like you, seem to have missed the ugly age altogether." She was ready to work at once, sitting beside me. She never gave anybody anything but an apron for a gift. All year long she was making her Christmas aprons, maybe because she, like most of her friends in that town, lived in a woman's world of working and slopping and splashing and wiping up. It *was* odd she never came by the kitchen door.

Right away, before Phyllis had done even one pan, Mother said, "I'm clean out of coffee, imagine that." And to me, "You need a change. Why don't you go and get some?"

I never liked going for coffee, because drinking coffee was a sin and the grocer was a good Mormon, one of the officers in our Ward. Dad said, once, when I objected, "He *sells* it, doesn't he? If he's such a Saint, why does he sell it? Like old Brigham Young and the still they say he had up in Salt Lake Canyon!"

Dad was a Jack-Mormon, or he never would have married Mother. His folks didn't like the way coffee and tea were drunk in our house, but Mother was not a Mormon at all, as he liked to point out to them, so whose business was it what she drank? When she went to the Presbyterian services with Phyllis, coffee was served right there in the church. "You'd think it was one of the Ten Commandments," Dad would say. "I've seen in an old newspaper how the Prophet Joseph Smith himself sold coffee in his store in Nauvoo."

But I still didn't like to buy it. I envied my best friend, who was the Bishop's daughter; she never had to buy humiliating things like coffee and tea.

I had never before wanted so passionately *not* to go to the store. "Mother, do I *have*—"

"Please," she said. "It's only a step. I wish I'd remembered. . . ."

"She could go and get some at my place if she wants," Phyllis said.

I felt their eyes meeting over my head. They wanted to talk without me there.

"It's on the pantry shelf, right in front," Phyllis said.

"I don't want to use your coffee," Mother said. "I need some for dinner anyway. And I need some other things." She picked up the pan on my lap as if it were settled. "Heavens, you're all wet," she said. "You'll have to change your dress."

I went into the bathroom to wash the fuzz off my wrists, which stung with it in spite of all that scalding. I made suds in the bowl and stood idling, looking down at my hands in the white soap, covered as if I wore gloves. Suddenly I heard the tinkle of the bottles outside and turned my head quickly and looked at the window. Mother was getting another batch. If there had been the least sound last night I would have heard it. I was just sitting in the tub, washing myself, facing the window. My washcloth dripped suds, the way I liked to have it, so I was covered with soap, even up into my hair. I had splashed and rinsed, letting the water run and run. And I had stood up at last to reach for my towel.

My name was embroidered on my towels. Mother had done this for a birthday present because she was particular and because my brother never seemed to notice what towel he used, and never seemed to bother to really wash his hands. I always folded my towels so my name hung in full view, in small letters across one corner, as in a hotel. "After all, you can *see* my name!" I would cry when I found it dirty and wet. "Mine are *pink*, anyway—mine are *pink!*"

I had put out a fresh one before my bath. It hung on the

single long rack by the basin, across the narrow room.
My feet still in the water, I reached over— When I
straightened, the towel in my hand—What had made me
look up? Did I always look up or had there been a sound,
after all, that I did not now remember?

I stood paralyzed, with my wrists in the suds. Maybe
every time I had a bath, for weeks and weeks— I had
never happened to look before, that I remembered. But
that table had never been there before, I thought, relieved.
And surely I would have noticed, because the face was
pressed to the window with the light full upon it. Two
eyes. I remembered how my own eyes had set, shocked,
and how I drew the towel quickly over my breasts and
how I lifted my hand to search for the string that would
pull out the light. It was as if I *waved*, searching for that
string, because it didn't seem to be where it always was,
somehow, and I had finally to turn and look up to find it.
And even before the room was plunged into darkness, I
heard the thud of feet landing on the wooden cellar door,
a crashing of bottles, and then silence, except for water
gurgling into the opened trap, and a murmur of unaware
talking and laughing from the living room.

I heard Phyllis' voice, shocked, and then it fell, and I
knew Mother had said, "Don't let her know we're talking about it, please." But I had heard what Phyllis said. "I
don't know of a stranger in town, do you?"

Of course it would be simpler if there were a stranger
we could blame, somebody who was different and who
would soon go away. The watchman wanted a maniac
and Phyllis wanted a stranger.

When I came back into the kitchen, Phyllis sat with a
scarlet, altered face, looking steadily down at her fingers
working in the pan among the fruit. Phyllis had goiter,
she had had an operation once, and her eyes had a peculiar
bulge rather familiar in our town. We were given pills at

school because our mountain water lacked something, iodine I think, but rather a lot of adults became victims before this was discovered. I had grown used to Phyllis' eyes and had stopped noticing them particularly, but that morning I could see the balls standing from her face, huger than they had ever seemed before. Suddenly I felt my clothes falling away in her mind. She *knew*. She was thinking how I had looked when the stranger stared into the window.

"There's change on my dresser," Mother said.

I was already on my way.

On the bright street I clung to the shade, hurrying from tree to tree. Our street was lined with Lombardy poplars, as most streets are in little Utah towns. How this happened I have never found out; I only know that the tall, slim trees with their quivering leaves are more common in Utah than they are in Lombardy itself. They were wonderful when we played out at night, especially when we played Run Sheep Run. We could slip along from shadow to shadow without being seen. But now—I knew I would never dare to run in the dark again. I remembered once when we were playing in a square we called the County Block, a grove of cottonwoods, and when I was It, searching for the others, a figure had suddenly stepped out from behind a tree, frightening me terribly. It had been a little boy who thought I had discovered him already. But now, I knew I would never dare to run in the cottonwood grove again, either, never as long as I lived. There was a story about a girl who was attacked in that grove, on her way home one night. . . .

My brother came along the street in his noisy, jazzed-up Star, his best friend Tom beside him. Tall for his age, Tom had to bend to fit into the little bug with its canvas top, his head forward from his shoulders, like a turtle. The car pulled up beside me, and they both laughed and held up strings of rainbow trout they had caught that morning in the creek. They had gone before dawn; now I remembered.

Mother would be pleased. I smiled, too, thinking how good the fresh fish would taste for lunch, cooked quickly in hot butter. Over his string, Tom's eyes were proud, but as I looked at him he suddenly blushed. His eyes fell.

Tom? He too— My knees went weak as I turned away and they drove off down the street.

As I began walking again I saw a man coming toward me. He was alone, somebody I had never seen before. He was tall and thin and I could see his face in the shadow of his Texas hat. A stranger? Before he reached me I turned quickly and leaped across the ditch and hurried across the street. I did not notice a boy on a motorbike until he swerved and yelled at me. I knew him. He was in my class at school. He dragged his foot and stopped the bike and called good-naturedly, "You wanna get killed?" And he laughed and was off again.

The stranger stood still, watching. And when I looked back at him I recognized him, after all. He was a nice man, injured in the war and without work a good deal of the time. He had one stiff leg. He could never climb onto a table as high as that. He smiled at me and I smiled back. Sometimes my father gave him work when there was an extra gang on the railroad. He had called at our house once for his pay.

As I came into the grocery store, a man was coming out. He was of average height, but taller than most women, and carried a heavy box bristling with produce. A farmer who had come in to do the weekly shopping. His eyes looked at me over the bundle, and he turned his head as I passed. I felt his look upon my back.

I was being silly, I knew it. There was *only one.*

When I came to the counter, the grocer said, "Hello

there, how are you?" as he always did. He didn't wait for
my answer, but leaned on the counter and looked at me.
"I hear you had some trouble at your house last night,"
he said kindly. He was an old friend. "It's been a long time
since I've heard of a prowler in this town." Cluck-cluck
went his tongue. A terrible thing. And over me went a
wave of itching heat, as if the peach fuzz had settled on
me everywhere. I only nodded, my tongue absolutely tied.

"What'll it be?" he asked, and I wished it were not
coffee today. Especially today, for some reason. He always looked disapproving, or anyhow, I thought he did.
I was glad I didn't have to get any pipe tobacco today;
sometimes I had to ask for that and if anything was
worse than drinking coffee it was smoking tobacco. But
Dad liked his pipe. Sometimes, right on Sunday, he smoked
a cigar after dinner and when I came in with Carol after
Sunday School she stared at him sitting with his newspaper
in a cloud of smoke.

My fingers trembled, taking change. On the street again,
I began to run.

In front of our house the boys were still sitting in the
bug, talking and laughing together. I slipped into our
yard through the hedge at the corner and crept along the
ditch, then darted unseen to the kitchen door.

While they drank their coffee, Mother and Phyllis talked
of dozens of different things. I went to work again. And
before it was time to fry the fish for lunch there was a
long row of bottles filled and cooling on the table, every
peach face down, tender and transparent. Mother counted
them proudly. "They'll taste so good this winter," she
said. She always said that, every time she finished jelly or
pickles or any kind of fruit. She insisted that Phyllis
should stay and share the fish.

When Dad came home he brought some paint for the
upper bathroom window.

"It'd be too dark painted," Mother said. "Phyllis suggested we get one of those curtains that lets the light in but nobody can see through. And we can put up a blind for night. I don't know why on earth we never thought of having a blind in there."

The fish were frying when somebody knocked at the screen. It was our next-door neighbor, old Mr. Ricky, with an armful of new corn. "It's just right now," he said, "and I said to Mrs. Ricky, this is the time to give it away, when it's prime. We can't eat it all. It gets too old in a day."

He was long and bony, his knees bent in his worn jeans. I had seen him hundreds of times, on his knees transplanting incredibly fragile plants; in the yard cleaning the cages of his many canaries and budgies; walking to church beside his wife, repeating to her in a loud voice everything people said, for she was very deaf. One Christmas he brought Mother a thin little poinsettia he had raised in the sunroom of his house.

"They say the only way to get corn absolutely *right*," he said, "is to boil the water while you pick it, and then to shuck it as you run."

His eyes darted around the kitchen as he laid the green ears on the table, and seeing me, suddenly began to blink. He leaned awkwardly forward and began to pick at the delicate corn silk that clung to his clothes.

"Let me pay you something," Mother said, because his wife was always complaining about how he gave everything away.

"No, no, it'd only get too old if it wasn't eaten," he said. "Two old folks can't eat a whole patch of corn."

"It can be dried—"

"We've got dried corn from years back," he said. "I told her I wasn't going to stand the mess and flies this year, not until all the old corn's used up. We've got a gunny sack full in the cellar." As he went out I saw him pause and look at the table, at the window; he stumbled as he started along the path. He stepped over the low fence between our yard and his.

He hadn't been one of the neighbors to help look last night. Several had come over, seeing the lights moving around the yard, but the Rickys' bedtime was soon after sundown, and they were up, as Mr. Ricky liked to say, with the larks. Who told him, I wondered. And the grocer. Who told *him?* I remembered a little play we had put on once at school. It was called *Spreading the News,* and it was about a little town like ours, full of gossips who made things worse and worse and worse with every repetition.

"Would you mind shucking that corn?" Mother asked me. "I've enough water boiling to get it on right away. Do it outside, will you, it's terrible for drawing flies. Peaches are bad enough."

Work and work. Dad smiled at me and came to help.

The fish was wonderful and so was the fresh corn. But I was not hungry. Tom ate with us, and with him and Phyllis to add to the talk, nobody noticed whether I ate or not. Twice during the meal the telephone rang, both times for Mother. She talked in a low voice and came back to the table. I saw her frown at Dad and I knew people were calling to ask questions. To say how terrible, maybe. Friends, relations.

When the dishes were done I started for my room, just as the telephone rang again. "It's for you," Mother called.

Carol. I had thought of going to her place and had decided not. Had she heard too? I trembled as I said hello. But she had just got back from a canyon trip, an overnight, and only wanted to tell me she was home again. We had dresses alike that summer, two of them, and she wanted to know whether my yellow one was clean. "Let's wear them to Sunday School tomorrow," she said.

Sunday School.

"I don't think I can go tomorrow," I said. "I—"

"Our class is singing, you've *got* to go," she said. "What's the matter? You've always—"

I wanted to tell her but not over the telephone, not with the family listening. Not with Tom right there in the room, still talking and laughing with my brother. Besides, people said the operator listened to conversations and never missed a thing that went on in our town.

"I'll come over," I said. "Later."

But I knew I could not go to Sunday School. Stand up and sing? I could see the rows and rows of faces. I could see the rows of eyes looking, looking, looking, and when I noticed them they would look at the books in their laps. In front of me and in back of me and on both sides. Every one of the tall— But not in the church. *He* wouldn't be at church. Maniacs didn't go to churches. And strangers just went through town, sometimes on the railroad, riding the rods. Tramps. It had probably been a tramp from the Hobo Jungle, down by the tracks, and he had seen the light in that window. He had gone off, scared, on the early freight.

But the sheriff said it was somebody who knew the place.

Tomorrow I wouldn't go, and then not for a few weeks. People forgot soon, like they forgot about poor Mr. Darcy, whose books at the bank had been found "wrong-on-purpose," as people said. Whose house was taken away and whose wife went off and left him and who finally came back to church and shook hands with everybody, hard, stiff as if his arm were an old broom. Afterward, Carol's mother had said, "People are so nice in this town.

They were good to him, weren't they? It's a good-hearted town."

I tried to rest but every time I closed my eyes I could see the face. It hung there behind my lids, in the dark, just on the edge of being somebody I knew. Dad was in the bathroom, measuring the window. The telephone rang again and again.

The Vision of Uncle Lars

"How did you meet Uncle Lars?" I asked one day, and Great-Aunt Anegrethe smiled at me over her fine coffee cups.

She looked pleased to be asked, and why not, for just then I was the freshest audience in the world. At sixteen, love is everything and one feels poised on the edge of the great adventure. I was reading avidly about love, searching for romance in the library and out of it, wanting to know how all lovers had met. My mother's romance with my father enchanted me. Imagine— He lost his job because he was late so often from walking with her after lunch each day.

Aunt Anegrethe's blue eyes looked intent as she leaned over the table. "How we met at first— Well, it was not important, in crowds, for we were both Danes and the Danes got together in those days, to eat and drink properly for our festivals and to speak the old language. But if you are asking how we happened to find out we were *meant* for each other—"

"Yes—yes—" That was what I most wished to believe.

Out there somewhere somebody was waiting for somebody else. For *me*.

"But maybe you won't believe it," she said.

I cried, surprised, "Of course I'll believe it!"

"It's a *strange* story." She studied my face almost war-
ily. "Some people seem to think that Lars made it up,
that he might have had a dream."

As far as I was concerned, there was nothing wrong
with dreams.

"If Uncle Lars said it was so, it was so," I said stoutly.
After all, he had been a man of substance in our very
substantial world. I remembered the day he died, altogether too young to die, everybody said, and the day of
his funeral. It was held in the Provo Tabernacle, which is
significant. In Utah, an ordinary funeral will be held in
the Ward Chapel, but when the deceased is of great importance only the Stake Tabernacle—a conference place for a
number of Wards together—will hold the crowd.

Children take pride in mourning, in being part of a
group getting all of the attention. My affection for Uncle
Lars had been thick with pride, anyhow, for he had immense dignity along with his Danish warmth. He had
been Superintendent of Schools and the sight of his portrait over the stairs in the schoolhouses could bring up my
chin the way the solemn portrait of his father could.
Great-Grandfather wore a Dannebrøg medal given him
by the King of Denmark for gallantry in a far-off war
called Slesvig-Holstein, and when I looked at it I felt I
was as good as anybody on earth, if not a little better.
There was a brave story of his journey across the plains
in the early days, and another about his abiding love for
his Danish Johanna. He was never converted to polygamy,
though he bore a ringing testimony to most Mormon doc-
trines, and when Brigham Young advised him to take a
second wife (since he could afford it and she wanted him)

he complied to the extent of a ceremony and giving her his good name. But according to the family legend, he fitted out a small house for her, with Johanna's help, and never so much as spoke to her again. Her maintenance was attended to as long as she lived, arriving promptly every month, by mail. It was years after I first heard this story, when I began to give heed to the various special sorrows of womankind, that I thought of this poor lady, alone and rejected in her little maintained house. It was Aunt Anegrethe herself who brought her to mind one day. "Polygamy and the Word of Wisdom—we Danes didn't take to either one," she said.

The Word of Wisdom forbade coffee, along with tea and beer and a few other amenities. But to Danish converts coffee was sacred in its own way, and unto the third generation this special sense of its value has not yet entirely disappeared. Coffee is the heart of breakfast, the true beginning of the day. It is the soul of late afternoon when work is finished and friends and relations can gather over a table laden with fine pastries and thick cream and sugar, all set out splendidly in Royal Copenhagen china on a white linen cloth with a bouquet of flowers in the center and more often than not, especially in wintertime when dark falls early, candles burning. There is laughter and relaxed conversation. Good bread is brought from the oven in the nick of time, its incomparable fragrance the natural twin of that aroma sweeter than any other, coffee just come to the boil. It is made properly in an open pot, the grains held by egg beaten with its shell, so the coffee is settled and sparkling and clear.

Over their cups, Utah Danes had a gentle rejoinder to those unfortunate orthodox who sniffed unappreciative noses: "Brother Joseph never meant that Word of Wisdom for the Danes!"

Once Aunt Anegrethe, who had a historical bent,

pointed out to me in a book about early Mormons that the Prophet himself sold coffee in his store in Nauvoo, Illinois, and that Brigham Young had served it in fine silver in the Beehive House. "They believed in the good life," she said. Once she triumphantly pointed out part of a journal by the wife of Colonel Thomas L. Kane, beloved in Mormon history for his intercession with the government during the Utah War late in 1857. Years later, Kane brought his wife to visit his Utah friends, and the journal she kept was published to help engender sympathy when the Mormons were worried over hostile antipolygamy legislation.

"Listen to this, it's about a dinner they were given right here in Provo!" Aunt Anegrethe said triumphantly. " 'We had a brave long grace before meat. I noticed that before uttering it President Young's eye had wandered over the table, to see every cover lifted, even the glass top of the butter dish. The stoppers were taken from the decanters of homemade wine. I once saw, at a Mormon dinner party in the city, the corks drawn from the champagne bottles which effervesced in accompaniment to the speaker.' " Mrs. Kane described the menu in detail, as impressive a dinner as any ever reported from a Danish feast. "And—" my aunt pointed out the end of it delightedly—" 'tea and coffee!' "

The day of her husband's funeral her own house had been fragrant with coffee as well as with many other good things Shakespeare would have called "the funeral meats." At the service a poem was read which had been Uncle Lars' favorite, and naturally, for it was a sea poem and Danish blood will always contain a good share of the sea. When I heard the familiar words, "And may there be no moaning at the bar, when I put out to sea!" I turned and looked at my aunt, for she was asked, certainly, to cease crying. And she had. She looked very red-faced and strong. Beside her, along the row, sat her children, and none of them wept again.

Why would I not believe any story she might tell, when I had been filled with wonder over stories of her life as far back as I could remember? Long before I became a student at the Brigham Young University myself, I knew from her how it had been there in her time, when it was Brigham Young Academy, in 1883. How easy our lives were compared to hers, for she had not only been obliged to make every dress she wore, but had woven the cloth as well. Besides, she had taught school for years before she ever got there. "I was thirteen when I was first hired to teach," she told me proudly, "and the schoolroom was a cellar with a dirt roof. I can still remember one of the grammar lessons in the book, I repeated it so many times: 'John's a noun because it is a name proper because it is an individual name. Boy is a noun because it is a name common because it is a general name.' And I can see the reading lessons to this day:

> 'John Brown flew his kite
> One very windy day
> When a gale broke the tail
> And it soon flew away.'

"I could recite to you the whole thing, all the trouble John Brown had with that kite. Somebody rescued it finally and the story ended:

> 'Up the tree climbed he
> And brought the kite down.
> "Many thanks, many thanks,"
> Said little John Brown.'

"Sometimes I got tired of teaching the ABC's over and over and taught the children to knit. Even the little ones, no more than five or six years old, could make good heels and toes. They needed lots of good thick socks, for we still wore wooden shoes to school the way we had in Denmark.

"But there was an old widow in Pleasant Grove who was a stocking knitter. If people had knitted their own socks she would have starved to death, so she complained to the Bishop about me teaching the children wicked things. I almost lost my job. The Bishop came to the school and told me to stick with academic subjects and leave the knitting alone."

The stocking lady, like all the other tradespeople, was paid in produce. Aunt Anegrethe remembered carrying over a pail of milk for a pair of socks, with a large piece of butter floating in it. "Sometimes people were paid in eggs, sometimes in cheese, and sometimes—" She clucked her tongue to tell it. "Sometimes we paid in good home-made beer. But it was true, as people said, that beer was healthier than water. Water came out of the ditches and flowed through corrals behind the houses. There were no clean *hesthusen* and *kohusen* like the ones in Denmark, but open places with pole fences or maybe small sheds of rough lumber or poles with straw for a roof. We had a log cabin at first, over here, but it had a huge cellar almost before it had a roof, for the proper care of milk and cream and butter and cheese. Our good farming—what I have heard described as 'the invisible baggage of the emigrants'—came right along with us to America."

One of the first eager questions I asked her was what she remembered about the ship. She sniffed and said it was fine except that it could have been more clean. "To get rid of the cooties was something! We Danes weren't used to such things and always claimed they were brought aboard by the English. But I remember how pretty the sun looked going down, like a gold piece set on the blue water. And I used to think the moon path on the water was the way to heaven."

Arrived in Utah, children had a happy life. "Better than now, for we made our own amusements then. Our own music, our own drama, everything. Once, when the church was remodeled, the organ was left at our house for a while, and before it was taken away I got to love it so much I was determined to have one. So I dried apples and peaches and picked ground cherries and wild choke-cherries and elderberries and sold them for good money. In three years I had an organ of my own."

She was not really very religious in the orthodox sense, even when she was a child. When they had long family prayers, everybody kneeling in a circle with hands folded and heads bowed on their chairs, she had various ways of amusing herself, like dropping seeds through a hole left in her chair by a brace and bit. Yet she was considered old enough to stay with the younger children when she was eight years old and the folks went to Salt Lake to conference. "I could cook well enough," she said, "but I hadn't yet learned to sew. Mother had some material, gray delaine we called it, that she intended for dresses for the girls. While she was gone I decided to make my little brother a suit, for a surprise. So I cut it out and sewed it up. But when it was finished I found I had forgotten to leave any openings for him to get into it. You should have seen Mother's face when she saw it. Father said, 'It's time that girl was taught to sew.' So I began, and by the time I was ten I made everything I wore, even to my winter coat."

Why should I not believe any story she told? She and Uncle Lars had lived in a different, a far more fabulous world than mine. "I promise to believe every word about you and Uncle Lars," I said.

But she frowned at me. "Don't ever promise to believe

anything," she said. "And until you're a good deal older than you are now, don't promise to love forever."

Even then I was far enough along to know that a promise to love could be a flighty thing. Today became tomorrow, not to speak of the day after that.

"When the time comes—" Her eyes altered, and her voice. "You will know. Sometimes I wonder that it took so long for me. When Lars and his father were on their way to Denmark for a mission, they stopped in Pleasant Grove, and I paid no more attention to one than I did to the other. Lars was so dignified and popular that I didn't suppose he knew I was alive, and perhaps he didn't, then. At the time I thought I was in love with another boy; ridiculous!

"We gave them a big dinner and practically the whole town came. Everybody had letters and gifts and messages for them to take back to the Lovely Land. I remember my father saying, 'When you go to the farm at Veddum, tell them I am well and my family is well too. Tell them Anegrethe remembers them all, even though she was such a little one when we came away. Tell them we speak of Denmark and the old home all the time, but we won't be coming back to stay now; it is turning out very well for us here.'

"'That will be a relief to them,' my mother said, because my father had been the oldest boy and when he came to America there was an arrangement made with his family. If he did not like America he could come back and take the farm of which he was the lawful heir; but if he did not return his brother Peder could claim it forever.

"So Lars and his father went away. Later we had a letter that they had gone to the farm and had seen the folks. Everybody in town had such letters from missionaries, and I didn't think twice about Lars' visit to the old folks until he came home again. It was two years later, even a little more than two, when he and his father were in Pleasant Grove again, bringing messages and gifts. Uncle Peder had sent us some fine things from the farm; I use some of the cups even now, as you can see. We were grateful to Lars and his father for taking such trouble for us. What luggage they must have had! But they shook their heads when we thanked them and said there had been no limit to the permitted weight, between them, and it had cost them nothing but a bit of energy which otherwise would have gone to waste.

"During dinner I couldn't help noticing that Lars kept looking at me. Whenever I lifted my eyes I was apt to meet his, and during the toasts especially I felt how his look lingered longer on me than on anybody else. Mother noticed, too, and smiled and poked me with her elbow and said, 'Lars seems to think you look well enough tonight.'

"So it was no surprise when dinner was over and he came at once to speak to me. 'Anegrethe,' he said, 'you will be surprised to know that I saw you in Denmark.'

"My mother laughed and said, 'Was there somebody who looked like her, there in Jutland?'

"But he shook his head. 'No, there was not. That is the strange thing.' And he told it for the first time. 'I was there at the farm in Veddum, and they had a big dinner, as fine as this one tonight. Afterward, Peder walked with me to the gate of the big house, through a garden of flowers. There we stood, talking, saying goodby and making arrangements about the things I was to fetch back to America with me. It was about ten o'clock, and still light the way it is around midsummer—you know the kind of shimmering light at that time of year. I was facing the house. And then—then, of all strange things, Anegrethe came out of the front door and stood there, looking out at us.'

" '*I?*' I burst into laughter.

"But Lars looked soberly at me and at Mother and at Father, who had come to listen. 'I said to your uncle, "For heaven's sake, you didn't tell me Anegrethe was visiting you." I had told them about you and your family at dinner and it struck me as odd that they wouldn't have mentioned such a thing. I had been eight months from Utah and there had been plenty of time for you to come there. But your uncle said, "Ane is not here," and turned and followed the way I looked. The girl stood there for a minute, all in white, and then she walked down the steps and went around the house. "Well, I have no idea who she can be," your uncle said. "She is a stranger to me." But he admitted she looked like one of the family and we went around the house together to find out who she was. But she had disappeared. So we went into the house and asked. But the women said nobody had been there. Nobody at all.'

"When he told that part of it he was looking over the top of my head as if he were seeing it all over again. When he dropped his eyes to mine, in a silence that covered us all, they were questioning and he frowned. 'What do you think of such things?' he asked.

"A strange feeling went over me, from head to toe. You can imagine. Mother laughed and said, 'It must have been *some*body.'

" 'It was Anegrethe. Tonight I knew for sure, the minute I saw her. And something else has happened.' It was as if we were alone in that crowded room and he spoke only to me. 'You have changed,' he said. 'I had not remembered you were so pretty.'

"I was blushing and trembling by that time and people were standing around us. My father said, 'Anegrethe dreams often that she is in Denmark again. When we left there I thought she would never stop crying. In New

York she sat and wept, there at the Immigration—for a Danish pancake! But of course I could not find one. I brought a pie at last—'

" 'She hated it,' Mother said, 'because it was full of prunes, and too thick altogether.'

"A silence fell. I could not think of anything to say. Lars took my arm and said, 'May I see you home?' People watched us go out together. And in a week we were engaged. And in six months we were married."

I sat very still. I had promised to believe.

"Years later, we went to Denmark together, only a little while before Lars died. We stood together by that same gate with my Uncle Peder and he remembered very well what had happened there. Lars looked at me and smiled when he spoke of it and I was surprised that the door did not open and the girl come out again, the picture he had painted was so real to me. It was as if he read my mind, which is something I always believed he could do, for he often knew what I was thinking before I had time to say. 'How could she come out again now, Ane?' he asked. 'She is here beside me now.' And he put his arm around me as his way was during all those years. . . ."

Aunt Anegrethe ceased speaking and sat smiling over the Danish cups, the white and blue. When I did not speak, she said, "Will you have more coffee? But I'm afraid we need some more; we've let it cool in the pot."

She rose and went to the kitchen, which was still fragrant with her baking bread. Returning, she smiled as she poured me a hot cup. "The next time, I will make you Danish pancakes," she said.

The Secret Summer

It was under a full moon on a warm evening in July that I fell in love for the first time. He was a neighborhood boy I had always known, with the brisk and manly name of Kirk. He rode a horse around town every day, delivering the Salt Lake *Tribune* from a swinging canvas bag. He was in my class at school and I had even thought of him, now and then, as being rather dumb. But most boys were sometimes dumb in school, somehow not caring—amazing to the girls in my crowd, who compared marks more jealously than dresses clear up to the portals of high school. Perhaps the substantial rewards for scholarship (never in money but in praise and gifts at home) contributed to my ambition in that direction, but a good deal of it was simply contending with the other girls. One of them, a girl named Phyllis, constantly threatened to outdo my string of A's. And then the arrogance and superiority of boys on the playground was hard to bear. Until that summer.

Just before I was promoted to the sixth grade, my teacher had paused one day at my desk. "I liked your poem," she said in a low voice. "Maybe you'll be a writer some day."

It was an unforgettable moment. After school I stopped at the library and selected some books of poems to take home. And in my journal I made an excited entry with an illustration. The poem the teacher spoke of had been printed, actually printed, in the *Juvenile Instructor*, a magazine published in Salt Lake City. Carol had sent it in and so became responsible, as I tell her to this day, for the infection of print which has never left me.

But in the diary I wrote: "I am going to be either a writer or a violinist. I think I'll work on both and leave the rest to The World and Fate." I illustrated this sturdy sentiment with stick figures, one with a fiddle, one at a desk with a feathered pen, between them a large "*Which?*"

The World was never subjected to my fiddle, for no child on earth ever brought so little so passionately to an instrument. For a year or so, Mother heroically insisted on daily practice, for she dreamed of a trio of sisters, Helen piano, I violin, Geraldine 'cello. But nevertheless the poor woman firmly closed the kitchen door whenever I began to tune up. My violin she arranged to buy from a German convert who lived in the mouth of the canyon and ran the electric plant. His name was Brother Brox and his whole family was musical, he himself beguiling his lonely hours with lively tunes on his zither.

It was an illuminating session with my teacher, Miss Winifred Parry, one bright summer afternoon, that left writing indisputably in possession of my ambition. I had been learning positions and had come at last to the lesson on vibrato. All week I vibrated conscientiously, for was not vibrato the key to violinistic emotion? I played records on the Victrola, listening over and over to an Ave Maria with a shivering violin obbligato, accompanying it as best I could. I vibrated up and down the scales and went over every piece in my book, wondering at how they were altered and improved by my new technique. By

Friday afternoon I was ready to show Miss Parry my immortal soul. She would, I fully expected, cry out, "Amazing! You should study abroad!" At the least I thought she might burst into happy teacher-tears.

To this day I can hear myself at the short warm-up scale, how I prepared for the revelation. With compressed lips and hot eyes, I began "Over the Waves."

Presently Miss Parry turned her back. I quavered on. I noticed that her shoulders were shaking. Proudly, I gave it all I had. And then, suddenly, she turned to me, her face scarlet with helpless laughter. She was one of those huge women with a round, pink face, very pretty, and shapely slender legs that never seemed to deserve the incongruous burden of weight above them. "Oh, *dear—*" she choked, and was off again.

So I knew.

It was bad pedagogy; I have learned just how bad it was, since, in Methods of Education I. But nevertheless I was given the kind of self-knowledge that must come to those whose romantic ambitions alone provide their artistic energy. In art, a certain truth is there from the beginning, and no teaching can supply its lack. Still loving the instrument, I have played in orchestras, whenever I have been able to find one small and desperate enough, but ever since that day I have known the truth, bending an ear to my quaverings over the thunder of instruments to the rear. And I am grateful for knowing what I know, for the music of violins is to me an endless miracle, a great player the first wonder of the world.

The next summer my realistic mother also realized the truth and abandoned, with me, her trio of the three sisters.

So it was that poetry came into full possession of the field of my life's ambition, presiding alone at the birth of love.

The afternoon of the fatal evening I was wading on our lawn, keeping cool over the pleasant duty of seeing that the ditch, turned into our lot for our water turn, flooded all the right places. Between turns, in midsummer, brown spots would appear if they had been neglected.

I heard the whistle of the afternoon train from the north and knew the paper boys were on their ponies, galloping to meet it. Every day that train brought the *Salt Lake Tribune* and the *Salt Lake Telegram* and the *Deseret News*, and within fifteen minutes, armed with swinging bundles, the rival delivery boys would ride the town, delivering papers onto porches with the precision of Indians delivering arrows. It was not long before bicycles took the place of the ponies, as black a day for romance as the passing of the Pony Express. A good paper boy could train his horse to know every subscriber's house. I had heard Kirk claim that aboard his pinto he could ride his route asleep.

That day I waded out front as soon as I heard the train. I thought I was watching for the paper to get ahead of my sisters, with whom I fought for the funnies. I heard Kirk pounding along the street and knew when he threw our neighbors' papers onto their porches. I knew exactly when he would arrive at our gate, toss the paper, and go pounding on. But that day he paused, reining his horse in, and sat looking down at me with the paper in his hand.

"Your Dad sure gets mad if the paper's wet, don't he?" he asked. The horse, released, immediately lowered its head and began nosing the wet grass against the fence. I looked briefly up, and then admiringly down at the real cowboy-with-high-heels boots Kirk wore. All of the boys in his robust Gang wore them, swaggering. He held a thick rope bridle in his hand. "Wading?" he asked.

It was obvious, so I didn't answer, but my heart swung high. He leaned forward over the horse's neck, looking at me, smiling. "Heard you're a poet and don't know it," he said in a gentle, wheedling sort of voice.

I felt a surge of pride. Maybe he had heard what the teacher said. Maybe he had seen the big A at the top of my last poem. But he added, high on his horse, "Thought so, seein' your feet."

My feet? I glanced down at them, ugly and long and red in the cold water, among the grass. Kirk laughed suddenly, wildly, and said "*Long*fellow!" And off he went. Dust rose behind his horse as it flew up the street, a great cloud among the trail of his laughter. What did he mean, Longfellow? And then, once more, I knew.

Smarty! Smarty! Smarty! I hated him vividly; it went through me like a streak of lightning and my eyes grew hot with rage and tears.

But it was that same night, when we were playing out, that my hate altered into something else, something painfully tender and bewildered, for which I was never again to find a cure. Out of such vagaries of feeling come the sweet cruelties of man to woman and woman to man. She begins her strange, wise blunderings, and he becomes willing, gradually, as he becomes a man, to endure a measure of manly gentleness.

Playing out. What unforgettable summer nights! The moon rising over the mountains east of town was so huge it seemed unreal, especially when the dust of a dry day made it the color of blood. As it rose, it paled, becoming the familiar moon, our summer friend. Many places the moon appears flat, a set picture moon pasted upon the sky, but the clear air of mountains gives it true dimensions. I remember it hung among the stars like a bauble and how soon I knew it had as many faces as the earth itself. Seeing one face only, yet we loved to imagine from its configurations amazing seas and mountains and continents and had a game we played at parties, "What Would You Take to

the Moon?" Perhaps it was our generation that dreamed
the first real trans-space dreams. The shadows on the
moon made a face, but it was not the face of a man as some
supposed. It was the profile of a lady. She was like a
Gibson girl, lovely, with her hair dressed high for some
celestial ball, her throat long and white. I saw her for the
first time after I read an article in my father's union magazine, *The Railroad Telegrapher*. It had a photograph illustration showing The Lady in the Moon, and never
again did I see the flat, round moonface I had seen before,
but only that exquisite profile with its piled-up hair.

On a fine night a crowd would gather on the street after
supper. At first perhaps one or two met and they would
move, then, around the block, calling and clamoring at
every door.

"Mother—can we play out?"

"Right on our street, then. But don't you go as far as
County Block, you hear?" County Block was a grove of
cottonwoods between our house and the depot, and tramps
had been known to sleep there among the trees. We had
seen their cooking fires and had kicked blackened bean
cans out of the grass.

Run Sheep Run. Base on Fire. Hide and Seek. There
was laughter and shouting under street lamps fluttery with
moths that gathered on fly-specked globes in metal cages.
First the choosing of It, with loud counting, Eenie Meenie
Minie Mo! Then he remained, the Chosen One, as the
rest flew all directions to hide along ditches and fences
and around the corners of houses and behind lilac bushes
and trees that were in The Territory. We could hear It
and even sometimes watch him from our hideouts, leaning
against the lighted pole with his face in his hands exactly
like the figure in Tchelitchev's painting "Hide and Seek."

"One, two, three, four, five, six, seven! All good children go to heaven! Eight, nine, ten . . ." and on to one

hundred. Then he lifted his face and called in a piercing voice, "Ollie, Ollie, Ollie, *Here—I—come!*" He started out on his search, but never too far from home at the post, for if he went too far those with a chance to beat him there suddenly ran for it. If It touched you before you got Home you were Out; if you touched the post before he did you were In Free. One heard through the silence of the searching a sudden rush and then a voice like a bell stroke through the night: "In free! In free!" And presently, if some of the hiders were too long out, It would cry, "Alley, alley, alley, all in free!" But there were not many places to hide and a cautious It with good legs could capture us all.

I loved the hiding. Carol and I usually hid together. In the silence one could hear marvelous things—rustlings of dogs and cats wandering near us, distant stirrings and bleatings and callings and bursts of laughter and talk and horses running. Above us the night and its trillion stars swung from mountain to mountain. The grass smelled sweet and the sound of water running was music under everything. We could play until curfew, which was ten o'clock in midsummer. Many a time we lay silent in the grass when the fatal sound came, the clear tolling of the city bell. As it sounded its warning the children began to disappear, one by one, into their houses, and the mothers of slow ones who lingered to laugh and talk together began to call from their porches.

Just before curfew that night I was out hiding and Kirk was It. I heard him coming closer, closer, and knew I was the last, for I had heard the others caught, one by one; he was always a fast and clever It. He did not see me and walked on past. I waited until I knew he would turn, giving myself the most possible time, and then I leaped to my feet and began to run. He was after me, hard. And just short of the pole, I felt the merest brush of his hand.

. . . But I touched the pole, nevertheless, and shouted, "In free! In free!"

"I touched you!" Kirk cried. "I got you long before you—"

"You did *not!* I touched it first—didn't I, kids? You kids saw—" I appealed mostly to Carol, who would lie for me if necessary.

"I got you before you were past there, and you know it!"

"You were clear by that fence when I came in. If you'd touched me—"

He shouted defiantly over my voice, and I tried to drown him out. "In free! In free!" Everybody began to yell at everybody and mothers began to appear on the porches along the street. My own mother, hearing my voice, very likely louder than any other, called my name.

"Come on, you guys," Kirk said in a bitter, superior tone to his Gang, and they were scattering and disappearing. Why had I spoiled everything? Doors slammed. Silence settled.

On the way up to bed—I had been ordered there at once—I was still quarreling the quarrel. "Kirk didn't touch me, he didn't. He's an old liar."

"What difference does it make?" my sister demanded. "It was just a game."

"I don't *care*— If he'd touched me, I'd have known, wouldn't I? I'd have known."

Yet within myself I knew I had been touched. The place, on my right shoulder, was set apart by that knowledge and in the dark, under the covers, I thought in despair, "Now he'll be mad at me forever." Along my legs I felt the tired aches that my grandmother said were growing pains.

"Tomorrow when he passes," I thought miserably, "I'll go out and say I'm sorry. No, I won't—" I couldn't. I must make him believe I never felt him touch me or he'd know for sure I had lied. Now the Gang would never come and play with our crowd again. That's what I had done, lying again. Spoiling everything. But I hated him. Smarty!

I became fascinated with the heat of my tears running down onto the pillow. But as soon as I watched for them they stopped, and I could not make them come again, screw up my face as I might, thinking of Kirk and the quarrel. "Well, on the Twenty-Fourth he'll see me on that pretty float in the parade," I thought. I would be sitting in the sego lily right on top of the float my mother's committee of the Ladies' Literary Club was making. Every year there was a float called "Utah's Best Crop," and this year it was to be all kinds of flowers with kids sitting in them, but of course the sego lily was the top one, since it was Utah's own flower. My hair would be in curls instead of in braids, with a big ribbon. Kirk would think, "Maybe she got to the post before I touched her," because I would look, in my white dress, like a girl who would never tell a lie.

The moon rose and I could see it through the screen. Suddenly I sat up, startled. There was a cross over the moon. A cross! My eyes widened and my heart began a sick, hard beating. Maybe it was a sign. Just for me. It terrified me, coming, as it obviously did, straight from heaven. And as I lay there I heard something, a strange and eerie thing I had heard before, but never with my ears drumming with a terror of its meaning. It was an owl that my brother had recently discovered sitting in our barn. Now it was hooting accusingly in the moonlight.

I knew Who. *I.* I had lied because I was so mad at Kirk. I wanted to punish him. I wanted the kids to think I could run faster than he could and I wanted our side to win.

My sister turned over and I said, "Look—there's a cross around the moon," hoping against hope that she could see it too. But she was yawning in her innocence. "Maybe the world is coming to an end like those people said it was—it was in the paper—"

"Those people are nuts," she said irreverently. "And besides, the moon always has a cross around it when you look at it through a screen. Didn't you know *that?*"

I hadn't, but I wanted to. So I crept to the window as soon as she slept and opened the screen. It was true. Serenely free of any sign, the moon floated in the sky. But when I lay once more with tight-shut eyes, the owl began once again to ask his intolerable question. Mother and Grandmother were sitting on the porch, talking. I could hear their murmuring. Grandmother had come only a few days before and they had a lot to talk about. I worried about Grandmother a good deal, for she was an apostate by her own admission, and it occurred to me suddenly that perhaps it was her presence in the house to which the owl objected. Of course the owl had come a few days before she did—but maybe for a warning—

The ache in my legs got worse and worse and I turned over and curled up for a while and then stretched out. My sister was always complaining about having to sleep with me. She said I not only wiggled, but snored whenever I lay on my back. Now she lay sweetly sleeping, and my little sister too. I was the only horrible, obnoxious one; nobody would ever want to marry me or anything. Slipping out of bed, I said my prayers again, on my knees. We had learned the Lord's Prayer as soon as we could talk and I have never been able, to this day, to go to sleep without at least thinking those familiar words from beginning to end. If Our Father is in heaven, all is right with the world.

Mother's voice came clearly from the porch below. "All

Utah flowers. Paintbrush. Goldenrod. Wild rose. Sister Petersen is clever at designing things like that. She wrote the pageant too."

Grandmother said something about how lovely.

"It'll be a lot of work, but we figure we can do it in a couple of afternoons."

"These women work fast. I remember how fast they can make a quilt—remember that light and shadow design they made in one long day?"

I moved to the window so I could hear better. And I was rewarded almost at once, for Mother spoke my name. "Budge is going to sit in the sego lily," she said.

Budge was my family name, started by my little sister who could not pronounce "Virginia." For a time I was Budginia and then every variation, Budgey, Budget, Fuss-budget. In the same family language, Geraldine got to be Gerry and even Go-Wild-Deena when she yelled. Helen got to be Lulu. The one rule seemed to be that nobody should be called his public name when he was safely at home. It was part of the privacy of love. There were other family words, too, several that I was surprised not to find in dictionaries. One was ninky. Mother would say, "Don't be a ninky," the way English people say, "Don't be a silly, darling." It was a loving reproof of a word. Or she would say, "You did a sloosky job of that floor," when we left corners unswept. That, I imagine, is from the same folk root as slinsky, which some of our neighbors said, with sloppy the common ancestor of both.

"She won't look so wild when I get her hair curled," Mother was saying. "Sometimes I wonder about her. You notice who started that trouble tonight."

Grandmother laughed. "Well, she's *interesting*," she said.

"Her father says she doesn't really lie, it's just imagination," Mother said. "Maybe so. She used to have an imaginary friend, before she got so thick with Carol. She called this friend Ruby and said she lived in the hall closet. Honestly, you'd have thought somebody was really there. At the table she had a little seat and food on a tiny plate. But of course that's a long time ago."

"She'll be all right," Grandmother said.

"Some of the women thought Carol should sit in the lily—she *is* the prettiest one of the girls, don't you think? But after all, I'm chairman of the committee."

My heart thudded painfully against the window sill.

"I always liked imaginative children," Grandmother said. "They turn out to be the best people in the end. Maybe she'll write or something."

"The others are more musical," Mother said.

"I remember the first time I came, that fall she was about three," Grandmother said. "I said, 'Look at the pretty mountains,' and she said, 'I sprinkled snow on them this morning.' I've never forgotten that."

"But I used to worry. She played alone so much. And she still carries piles of books to read in the hall closet."

They went on to talk of something else and presently came into the house and I hurried into bed before Grandmother should come upstairs. At once, I was dreaming. About a terrible owl. And at dawn, while the innocent sisters slept on, I was awake again. Quickly I slipped into my clothes, for nothing suited me better than to be outside when the sun rose over the eastern hills. And how beautiful the dew was before a step disturbed it. A web hung on the yellow rose bush, chains of jewels, and bees had begun to settle on the roses. I went through the back gate and along the furrows of the garden, which were dark with yesterday's watering. My bare feet left what we called Friday prints in the soft mud. Our two pigs, expecting breakfast, were grunting as I came closer, and I climbed onto the pen and scratched them with a stick I kept handy for the purpose. They loved to be scratched around their necks and down their backs, just as dogs and kittens did. I looked at the barn and thought about the owl.

When I went into its shadowy hugeness I could see nothing for a minute except sunshine coming like spotlights through the knotholes, making spinning motes in the air. My brother's horse made a little whinny to welcome me. I wondered whether that owl kept him awake all night. I looked up, searching where we had seen it before. And there it sat, very near, on the first rafter above the door.

I stepped back into the doorway, gazing up. There it sat in perfect stillness, talons curved, eyes unswerving and round. It was looking directly at me. Its eyes seemed to have gathered light together for their own piercing use, like jewels. And indeed they were set like jewels in a great disk of white feathers, and the disk was a heart with a thin line marking the center as if it had been cut in two. I moved, only a little, and the huge eyes moved also, following me. Sun shimmered in long lines upon spilled hay and made merry with the silken threads where spiders swung. Something mysterious moved across the floor and vanished. A mouse, I knew. Or a rat. The owl's head turned clear around, watching. Then its undeviating stare returned to me.

I backed out of the door. It was good to get back to the house and find my father stirring away at a nice, ordinary pot of oatmeal on the stove.

"What are you doing, up already?"

"I went out to see that old owl in the barn. He kept me awake all night, whooing."

"They always seem to come along when we need them," he said cheerfully. "Everybody's been complaining about the rats this year."

"Do owls always come where rats are?" I asked.

He smiled and said, "Seem to. They have to eat."

"Where do they come *from?*"

"Oh—well, I don't know. From anywhere they happen to be, I guess. You better look it up in the Knowledge books."

"How do they know where to come?"

"Good Lord, I don't know," he said. "They just seem to know, that's all. Like hawks. Maybe they can smell rats."

He laughed and I asked anxiously, "What are you laughing for?"

"Just struck me funny, what I said. I said maybe an owl could smell a rat, see, and there's an old saying—you've heard it. If somebody smells a rat, it means he knows there's something wrong going on, see, that something's not the way it should be. Something's rotten in Denmark."

"Oh." And my heart was thumping again so I could feel it clear to my neck. I rushed upstairs where my sisters still lay, sweetly sleeping, and I leaped upon them, crying, "Dad says you should come to breakfast *right now!*"

He hadn't, of course. Breakfast wasn't even ready yet. And I knew all through the ensuing battle that I was in the wrong again, lying again. Yet when I started out of the room, appalled by my own wickedness, I turned back with yet another falsehood. "That old owl in the barn— He flew down at me!" Even as I uttered the words I would have withdrawn them again, yet they came from me helplessly in a perverse delight.

"Really? Did he?" Helen did not really believe. She had got so she demanded proof from me. "I'll bet you bothered him," she said.

"No, I didn't. I just went in and looked at him and all at once he—"

"You did *some*thing to him," she cried. "You spoil everything, you always do. Mother said maybe he'd stay and his mate would come and they'd have their babies in our barn, like they did at Swensons'. And now *you—*" She was up, dressing quickly. And when she had gone, running to the barn to see for herself whether I had frightened the owl away, I stood in the empty room and vowed never to lie again. I didn't want the owl to stay, but now everybody would blame me if he went away.

Helen came rushing back to say the owl was sitting where he always sat. And at breakfast the talk was all of owls. There were various kinds, Claude said, full of superior wisdom like any Boy Scout. Some lived in the holes of small animals and very cleverly ate the babies of their hosts as these arrived, an uglier ruse than a cuckoo's. But others were good, like our owl, and sat in barns and raised their families and killed off all the rats and mice so people didn't have to set traps or worry any more.

Carol and I had a lot of secrets. We had a secret meeting place we called Post L.A., and it delighted me to say on the telephone, "I'll meet you in ten minutes at the Post."

"Where's the Post?" my sisters asked curiously.

But I only tossed my head and slipped out of the door and went by a circuitous route around the block to that particular telephone post above the corner bridge just midway between Carol's house and mine. It was not only our meeting place, but it bore symbols we had carved carefully one night with the aid of a flashlight.

Post L.A.

V and C

w-v

bd-p

IAFYDSTTA

We had written out a translation of this for posterity and put it in a small wooden box which we nailed, with appropriate ceremony, under the bridge.

Post Life's Ambition
Virginia and Carol
writer-violinist
ballet dancer-pianist
If At First You Don't Succeed Try Try Again.

This was to remind us constantly of the necessity for practice. We selected for Our Own a piece called Simple Confession, I learning it on my fiddle and she on her piano, and at certain hours we played for each other, over the long block we lived apart. For a whole summer we had that box, having instituted it in the first place to send secret messages during an epidemic of the flu. Not permitted to meet, we arranged our rendezvous by telephone. In the box we had a lot of old keys found in drawers at home and around these we rolled the scrolls of our secret notes. These were, of course, in a special alphabet we had worked out, with the key word "Hello," and as many variations as any code I ever heard about. The whole thing was exciting and time-consuming and gave to life that summer the lovely fillip of secret things.

We made fun of our enemies in our notes, made appointments and broke them, and wrote out feelings and fears that were perhaps more important than we knew. The evening after Longfellow, I wrote an angry declaration: N MFYJ PNWP! Hello, at the top of the note, was MJQQT, so the message translated I HATE KIRK!

Carol's interest was in a boy named Rex, who herded cows that summer, collecting them from each yard early every morning and taking them out to graze in his father's meadows just west of the tracks. Every evening they could be seen and heard, coming home again, driven by

Rex and his fine collie. Looking back, I can see how pic-
turesque this was, at dawn and at evening, the sort of
thing tourists gaze at, enchanted, in Swiss villages. Some
of the cows were belled and the music of their coming
got into my memory so that the sound of that particular
tinkling brings back the whole scene vividly. For Carol
it was the sound of romance as the sound of Kirk's horse
was to me. Working with Code 2, with Hello JGNNQ, Kirk
was MKTM and Rex was TGZ, which we decided to make
into secret names. We said "Muktum" and "Tugs," and
nobody of course knew what we were talking about, so
we made outrageous remarks by the dozen in front of our
friends and our sisters.

Not only the box under the bridge had its secrets, shared
by Carol and me, but there were secrets *from* each other,
especially once that summer when jealousy raged at the
Post and for one long, terrible week I was Untrue. Temp-
tation arose when Carol came down with a rash and a
fever that the doctor suspected might be scarlet fever;
the rumor terrified all the mothers in town and brought
about a rash of old tales. Carol's younger sister, Dixie,
was bundled out of the house and stayed with Aunt Ethe-
linda, two doors from us.

Dixie was a pleasant, buxom girl, better-developed than
either Carol or me. One day I was sitting on the porch
looking at some mementos my mother and father had
brought home from New York City earlier that spring.
There were postcards and programs and baseball scores
and among them a folder about The Ziegfeld Follies,
with pictures of a few of the girls in their fabulous and
scanty costumes. Even looking at these seemed pleasantly
wicked to me, and when Dixie saw them she said, "They
don't use much material in their costumes, do they?"
She was a sewer; sewing was her life's ambition, as Carol
had told me disdainfully. But now Dixie gave me an idea

which made something special out of an empty afternoon. Nothing was more fun than dressing up, and we had
spent endless hours with old clothes Mother kept for the
purpose in a box in the hall closet. Hats with long feathers,
high-heeled shoes, dresses with sequins and rows of buttons and tucks and ruffles.

"Maybe we could make us a Ziegfeld Follies costume,"
I said.

Dixie looked at me and giggled and then we broke into
a perfect storm of laughter. Presently we were rifling the
drawers of my mother's sewing machine. We found dozens of wonderful things for our purpose, the best being
a roll of green silk left over from draperies along with a
piece of golden fringe. Over this we went into another
storm of mirth, because fringes seemed to be a great spe-
cialty of the Follies. We went to work with the door of
my bedroom closed against interlopers, a chair propped
under the knob.

This episode is commemorated in the journal with an
illustration. "Dixie and I sewed all afternoon. We are making us costumes. They are rather scanty, consisting of
nothing but breast pads all ruffled up with tassels and of
little tights that are about 5 in. up and down."

The next day we went to Beehive Meeting. "We had a
good lesson on *health*," says the diary. "We learned to
leave brassières and high heels alone." But afterward,
"Dixie and I sewed and finished our costumes."

The next entry brings back a scene that is as vivid as
any other in my life. "Carol is better today! She came
over when I was ironing and we went for a walk after
and I told her the story of the matinee she missed—Dream
Street. I do love Carol. She asked me about what I did
while she was sick, and if I missed her. . . ."

I can hear how she stammered it out, suddenly, as we

were about to separate at the Post. "Dix says you've been making costumes."

Why should she weep about that? I stood, amazed, and she sat down on the grass by the bridge. So I sat beside her. "Carol—"

"Don't speak to me!" she cried. "You two— Dixie told me all about it! Horrible little costumes like that! They're *nasty!*"

She jumped up and began to run toward home. For a minute I stood paralyzed, looking after her. It was so without warning of any kind. She stopped by the fence, leaning on her arms, and I rushed after her.

"Carol—"

"Don't touch me!" she cried. "You didn't even want me to know, did you? All the time I was sick, you and Dixie—" Before I could do more than protest she rushed on: "I told Mother about it— I told on Dixie and you too. She says Dixie can't even have those awful things in our house. *So!*" And she looked at me with a lofty pride, righteous and pure, and turned away.

I liked Dixie and for a moment my loyalty wavered. But maybe Carol was right, for I could think of nothing to shout after her. There *had* been a funny feeling about making those costumes, and there had been the barricaded door. "Carol—wait a minute!" I ran after her, clear to her gate. "Do you think I really care about that old costume? It was just fun, that's all, something to do while you were sick."

"Dixie says you even drew a picture in your diary!"

That sounded permanent and serious. We had laughed fit to die over those drawings, which didn't flatter us, heaven knew, or look anything like the queens in the Ziegfeld program.

"Come on," I said stoutly. "I'll burn the whole—"

Her breath was coming hard, from crying and running. "I'll wait for you at the Post," she said.

I ran all the way home and upstairs and down again. The tights weren't even finished yet, and as I picked them up out of my drawer a threaded needle pierced my fingers, a sure sign of the observation of a pained Providence. I tore off the beaded fringe, which Mother would object to losing, and under Carol's watchful eyes I vowed to be faithful, wrapped the offending Thing in paper, and solemnly struck a match to it.

"There!" I said.

But the picture in the diary remained. I made up for it in the next entry: "I love Carol so much more than I love Dixie. I have promised never to play Ziegfeld Follies again." And a few days later, "Another Beehive Meeting with Carol. Our lesson was 'Honor Womanhood.' We heard a wonderful description of Christ's mother, the Virgin Mary. She is my ideal. How I would like to be like her."

The prettiest girl in our class, and the one most popular with the boys, was named Marian. She had a big brother, Maynard, who went off to college in the East and returned, in an aura of sophistication, for the holidays. I have lost track of Marian long since and would never have thought of Maynard again if Marian had not turned one of his remarks into a moment of pure misery and sudden hate.

At recess one day she asked sweetly, "Do you know what my brother Maynard said about you?"

I was suspicious, but also curious. To my peril.

"He had a party when he was home," she said grandly. "He brought his roommate out. And they got to talking about the kids in this town." She was leading up to it as only Marian knew how. "He said you were—" she laughed helplessly—"as ugly as a mud fence." That was bad enough, and I recall vividly the wash of heat that went over me and into my offending face. But she wasn't finished with me yet. *"Plastered—with—pollywogs!"* she said.

Several years later Carol and I were still not speaking to Marian and neither of us ever chose her when we were It. Several ugly notes about her went under the bridge. Maynard's remark would still make me writhe about riding on that float, and to this day I think of him every time I have to sit for a photograph.

The Friday before the Twenty-Fourth, Carol and I went together to the matinee. The diary records that the picture was "Charley's Aunt," and that it was as funny as the ads promised—"enough to make a cat laugh." All I remember about it is that Marian came into the theater with her best friend and sat a few rows in front of us. Right after them, making a great noise, came Kirk and his Gang. They crowded into the row directly behind Marian and as the lights dimmed and the comedy began I saw her turning her head and Kirk leaning forward, talking to her, laughing. Not even a show that would panic a cat could keep my eyes from them after that. She kept turning around. He kept leaning forward. When the show ended he was teasing her all the way out and she was pouting and pretending not to like it.

"That silly Marian," I said to Carol. "How she acts with *boys!*"

"She's pretty," Carol said heartlessly. "And she has the cutest clothes in our class."

That night I told Mother I did not want to ride on the float, after all. But she frowned at me and said, "Of course you'll ride on it. I've finished your dress." And then my father came home with wonderful news that sent me tearing over to Carol's and all around the neighborhood. Ponies had arrived for the carnival and we were invited to ride them to the fairgrounds and back again; we rounded up ten kids for the purpose.

When we arrived, the ponies were already coming down a ramp from a freight car standing on the spur. Each one seemed handsomer than the last until I saw a certain one, coal black, with red ribbons braided into his mane. I stood close to him while he was saddled and was helped on. "There you go!" the man in charge said, and slapped my mount into line with the others.

That proud ride set the tone for the whole holiday. We went slowly along Depot Street to Main and then down toward the fairgrounds. Carol kept turning around to smile at me. She was on a white pony with brown spots. We slapped our pony's necks and kicked gently with our heels and called them by name. And as we rode, wonder of wonders, here came the Gang, riding along. Kirk was riding fastest, as he always did, and they all went around and around the line of ponies, like Indians around a train of pioneers. It was like a preview of the real parade to come next day, for they were to play Indians, as they had for several years already.

"Crazy kids," said the man who led the ponies. "Hey, you guys, take it easy, will you? Not so close—you worry the ponies—"

At the fairgrounds we watched the ponies put into a shed where they would be housed during the celebration, and then we walked around and saw everything. Concessions were going up, men were stringing bunting on the grandstand and putting up forms where the final fireworks would be set off, wheels were already beginning to spin and a shooting gallery was settting targets up. Prizes were being set out and we watched, entranced, as feathered kewpie dolls, the big prizes of that year, came out of their boxes. Never since have I seen a carnival with such wonderful prizes, for nothing can match the gay beauty of those plump, pretty, feathered dolls with their huge, lashed eyes and their elegant hair-dos. There were red-heads, blondes, brunettes, and some of them wore immense fans of bright feathers. For years afterward, these dolls brightened the parlors and piano tops of the fortunate winners.

One of the hawkers called to us. "Come and try, just a nickel, five cents, a prize every time!" And so we spun the first wheel. There were two kewpie dolls in the crowded circle of prizes, and as the wheel turned more and more slowly, ticking along a circle of nails with its little leather tip flipping—past the first kewpie, slowly, maddeningly, coming close to the other one—we had a tense moment of gripping hands between us. But the pointer came to rest by a small rubber ball on an elastic. "Here you are, a winner every, every time!"

"You can get those in a box of popcorn," Carol said disdainfully.

But I spent my last nickels to try again and again, taking home some more useless junk to add to my collection.

When I got there, another wonderful piece of news awaited me. The merry-go-round men and the Ferris-wheel men had given my father a whole roll of tickets after the cars were unloaded. These were distributed among us in strips of ten and seemed worth a fortune. Thinking of Carol, I folded my strips in two and found we could go free fifteen times apiece. And that very evening we began, showing off as we marched by the lines of poor, underprivileged kids who must wait and spend their money.

Around and around and around. It was so marvelous that I did not notice Carol's abstraction for a long time. There was a different horse to ride every time on the merry-go-round, and we pranced to the steady rhythm of the calliope, rising and falling, pretending to whip our mounts with the reins and looking at the marvelous pictures on the panels around the machinery and catching brief glimpses of our friends and relations out on the ordinary earth. We were riding the Ferris wheel for the fourth time, making the marvelous stomach-tightening ascents and the lovely, backward descents with the whole carnival spread like a magic carpet below and the white temple shining on its hill beyond—when Carol reached out and pressed my hand.

"Isn't this *wonderful?*" I cried, for our little car had stopped right at the summit while people got out and in below. "I don't care if we use every one of our tickets tonight, do you? There are a lot more things to do tomorrow."

"There's something that I—"

For the first time I was aware of her troubled face, but we had started down again, plunging into the deafening roar of the calliope playing "East Side, West Side." As we were once more lifted up, her agonized face had my full attention. "Dixie was mad at me," she said. "She's been jealous ever since you burned your costume. Do you know what she said to me—actually! She said she'd be glad if I got sick again and stayed sick all summer."

Our hands were linked between us and I pressed her fingers fervently as we went down and up again. "That was a mean thing to say," I agreed, and felt a twinge of guilt.

"And besides, she's jealous because you have all these tickets."

"I'll give her some. I should have given her some anyway," I said. After all, I owed Dixie a measure of loyalty for those happy, giggling hours we had spent together behind that barricaded door. For her clever needle too. Forever and ever, now, inescapably, Dixie and I had a secret too.

"No, you won't!" Carol cried passionately. "Because she's done the meanest thing." Her face was tragic, turned to me at the summit of the great wheel once more. We sat swinging gently and I felt the hot tremble of her hand. "She followed me when I took a note to our box. And after, she went and got one of your notes and she wouldn't give it to me. When I—"

"Carol—" My stomach and spirits were descending with the wheel, and Carol told me all. Dixie had threatened to tell about our box to everybody she knew if Carol did not explain the secret code of Hello. She promised she would give my note back and never take another and never tell a soul in the world if Carol told her everything. Even the meaning of the letters on Post L.A.

"She absolutely promised," Carol said. "And then to-night—she got mad about the tickets. I shouldn't have bragged, maybe—"

"But she had promised!" I said. "She didn't get my note *today*—did she?"

"I had to do the dishes before Mother would let me come—it was my turn—and Dixie went out on the bike. And she came back with that awful Marian and I knew *right away*—"

Marian. My heart stopped. The wheel went on turning. It stopped again, this time when our little car was on the platform, and the attendants began to open the bar and let us out. "No, we'll ride again," I cried, and thrust two more tickets into his hand. And on we went. I couldn't face the world just then. Not quite yet.

If Marian knew, everybody would know. She would tell Kirk and the whole Gang and they would all laugh. Every time I saw them they would be laughing. Because I had written a new truth that day. At dawn I had been writing, with my heart high and the carnival world full of promise. "MJQQT!" was the Hello. Because V went past the end of the alphabet with five added, my name began this time with an A, starting over. The message was contained in three revealing words: ANWLNSNF QTAJX PNWP. Virginia loves Kirk.

As the wheel turned, I sat paralyzed, looking into the crowd below without pleasure now and with a kind of terror. By this time they would all know.

"Let's get off the next time and go home," I said. I had a glimpse of a face that looked like Kirk's, looking up. I saw Helen, eating a huge cone of pink candy floss with her friends.

"Already?" Carol asked miserably. "I thought you said—"

"I've got to get my hair washed and put up," I said. Now the full enormity of riding in the parade on that sego lily came over me and left me sick at heart. I was wheeling through a world of wheels, the calliope keeping strident time. Guns were popping at the shooting galleries—that's where the Gang would be, most likely. Everything was going. Somebody yelled "Bingo!" as we got off. I could get sick, I thought, feeling sick already. Long since, I had learned that I could get sick at will and this time I would have an excuse. "Let's have a hot dog first; I'm hungry," I said, and dodged through the crowd to one of the stands. I ate two, covered with mustard and pickles and catsup, the works, and then I loaded myself with candy floss and a chocolate bar.

We slipped out of the crowd onto our own dark street. The calliope was wailing away at "Oh, Susannah!" and I was swallowing the last of my chocolate with determination.

"Even the words on Post L.A.," I said, on the corner.

"We can make some new ones," Carol said. "Honest, it was just to get the note back—she would have told everybody—"

"She's told everybody anyway."

As we parted we walked backwards, as always, facing each other until we were out of sight, like courtiers in a show we had seen. She was still calling, protesting that we could figure out a new code, and I was still forgiving her, for after all I was the guilty one, was I not? But for at least that one long night, I did not believe in a future at all. My mother knew something was wrong the moment she laid eyes on me. "You're pale. What have you been eating? Onions—I can smell *that*—"

"Chocolate. I can see that," my father said.

"I got sick on the Ferris wheel," I said, and it was true.

Grandmother offered to wash my hair and it was lovely to feel the warm water poured over my head, to feel her strong fingers on my scalp and around my ears and down. "You feel tight tonight," she said. "I'll give you a little massage." Her fingers ran comfortingly along the cords at the back of my neck. I leaned on the basin with my hair forward in the water, holding a washcloth over my eyes against the sting of soap.

"It was just because Mother was chairman I was put on that sego lily," I said.

"You have the prettiest hair in town, *that*'s the reason," she said.

I said nothing more. At the proper moment I would be too sick to go, and the stage was set. When I came into the kitchen I saw that my white dress was hanging up, freshly ironed, with a wreath hanging over it, the way people wear them when they go to Honolulu. All the time Mother was twisting my hair into rags, I kept looking up at it. After all, I had to look pretty in such a dress, and if I were riding in a lily, all in white, with flowers on my hair and curls hanging over my shoulders like Mary Pickford— Maybe Marian hadn't told Kirk, anyhow. Besides, when she was in love and kids teased her she acted as if she liked it;

sometimes she even intimated that the boy loved her back. I gazed up at the dress, and the hands twisting my hair made me deliciously and luxuriously sleepy, so that I sagged, dreaming, in my chair. "Hold your head up— just a minute more—" And my father was lifting me up and putting me in bed. And suddenly it was dawn.

A peal of bells. A thunder of guns. I thought, "It's today!"

Today, today. One waited and waited and at last it was today. The Fourth of July, Independence Day. The Twenty-Fourth of July, Pioneer Day. The Fair. Halloween. Thanksgiving. Christmas. My birthday. An exciting calendar of American Days, fiestas, celebrations, with things to do on every one that made it wonderful. I lay listening to the pealing of the bell, counting the strokes, for I had been told it would ring one time for each year since the Pioneers came. This was the birthday of the State of Deseret, which was much older than the state of Utah. This day commemorated the moment when Brigham Young saw Salt Lake Valley for the first time and said, certainly, "This is the place." Nothing had been growing here at all, but the Pioneers made it bloom like a rose.

I heard Grandmother and Father talking downstairs. She was almost as old as the State of Utah. It was hard to imagine, but it was true. Here, nothing was long ago. Today the parade would tell the whole story and real Pioneers would be honored. There would be somebody representing Brigham Young, with a long square beard, and there would be Indians and covered wagons and handcarts. And Utah's Best Crop, always near the end of the parade with the one called "And the Desert bloomed like a rose," which I had seen being made at one of our neighbors' houses.

I swallowed to see whether I was sick yet, for the

thought of Utah's Best Crop brought everything back to me. No, I wasn't sick at all; it took more than mustard with ice cream to sicken me. And now, in the full light of day with the bell ringing, I was glad, because how awful it would have been to stay home and miss everything. The parade was only the beginning, after all. There was a program in the Tabernacle at 11 o'clock, to honor the Living Pioneers, who would be given medals. After lunch the matinee, then the matinee dance and the ball game and the horse races and in the evening the pageant at the fairgrounds ending with a flourish of fireworks and everybody singing "Utah We Love Thee" with the band, and then, last of all, "The Star-Spangled Banner."

After all, I had to face Marian and Kirk sometime. It would be better to ride elegantly dressed in that lily and hold up my chin as if I didn't care whether they lived or died or knew every old secret in the universe. When Mother took down the rags and I saw the shining coils of my hair, it was settled and I had my courage back. Nobody would see my freckles at that distance, anyhow, and Mother said I could have a touch of lipstick and powder—just a little, like the time I was in the Primary Show. I gazed at myself, transformed, unbelieving, full of wonder that the angel in the glass could be me. I puckered my lips and pouted like Marian and felt beautiful with my shining curls falling over my shoulders, and the circlet of lilies.

It always took an age for the parade to form and get going. Wagons came from every direction and were moved into place by the chairman of the day. I sat stiffly in my flower and all of the other girls in theirs, waiting with our hands folded in our clean laps. I could see floats for two blocks ahead, and then the bright red of the high school band, straggling along tuning up. I saw the Indians moving into line and recognized Kirk in his war bonnet. His horse was gay with silver and leather.

I had never sat so still for so long, but for once I wanted those curls to stay put. I was sweating enough without moving.

At last the band moved ahead, the three drum majors prancing and the flag bearers strutting beautifully. After them came Miss Utah, standing on a hayrack float pulled by white horses. She was beautiful, the prettiest girl in the whole town, and people often marveled that she was bright as well, making an A record up at Brigham Young University. Today she was powdered to look like a statue and her blonde hair was dressed high in a coronet wound with golden ribbon. She clung to a pole wound with tinsel and sego lilies and over her head nodded a lily canopy.

After Miss Utah, the whole history of the state passed in review. Every organization in town had been given a piece of it to tell. The Boy Joseph prayed in the Sacred Grove, with two angels standing over him with outstretched hands, one of them speaking the words of the legend printed around the wagon: "This is my Beloved Son, hear him." That was the beginning of the Mormons, way back in New York when Joseph Smith had his first vision and the angels told him where to find the Sacred Golden Plates in a box buried in a hill. One float had the Hill Cumorah, with Joseph standing beside a golden box, facing backward on the wagon, his face uplifted. A smaller legend on that wagon said, "South Ward Mutual Improvement Association."

The Primary in our ward had done the Three Witnesses to the Book of Mormon, and I felt rather proud of it as it moved by. An angel stood pointing to a gilded book about six feet across, and Oliver Cowdery and David Whitmer and Martin Harris, dressed in jeans and straw hats to show they were simple, honest men, knelt before it.

"And we declare in words of soberness, that an angel of God came down from heaven . . . and we beheld and saw the plates and the engravings thereon."

Then came the Eight Witnesses, whose names I had memorized in Religion Class long since. Four Whitmers, three Smiths, and Hiram Page.

Then came a replica of the Kirtland Temple, made by the Genealogical Society. The real Temple was still standing, I knew, back in Ohio. It belonged to some bad people who had started another church, and had kept writing books that said Brigham Young was not a True Prophet of God. But our church had built a good many better temples since that one, so who was right and who was wrong? God wouldn't have smiled on us as He had unless we were the Right Church.

Now walked the American Legion band before their float, *Nauvoo*. This was the historic scene where the Prophet Joseph stood in his soldier's suit, holding a sword aloft, surrounded by his Nauvoo Legion. When it was necessary to fight, the Pioneers fought, the histories said. When the fighting did no good and the Prophet was killed in a jail in Bloody Illinois, the Saints took their worldly goods and came West. And the next float was a covered wagon, with men and women and children riding and walking alongside it dressed in old-fashioned clothes. Pots and pans banged, and even a curious dog trotted by the horses, making it all seem very real. Here was the whole Western story and people clapped as they went by, trailing their streamer: South Ward Sunday School.

The North Ward Sunday School followed with the famous handcarts which had become, as my grandmother said, the Mayflower of Utah, for everybody claimed to have an ancestor who had "walked every step of the way." My own Danish grandfather had really done it and my heart swelled with pride when I saw that one of the little

carts carried a fluttering Danish flag. So they walked a
thousand miles . . . and some were caught in the snow
up in Wyoming and died by the hundreds before they
could be rescued. Everybody seemed to have kept a journal in those days, and my own great-grandfather's was
a family treasure. "And when we arrived at last, leaving
behind all the dead, we found the miracle of the crickets
was perhaps true, for we were not troubled much by
them. But there had been no miracle with the hoppers,
and the crops were so poor our first year there was hardly
enough food for the people already in Zion. Jedediah Grant
said in a sermon that the hoppers were a rebuke from God
because people wasted their substance and complained of
the hard times. We were all baptized again. . . ."

After the carts came the carriage of Brigham Young,
bearing the legend "M Men, North Ward." My grandmother had seen that when she was a little girl; she had
told me about it, and how she was put into a white dress
and given a bouquet to throw in its path.

The Seagull Girls had made a fine white bird out of
white crepe paper, with a very realistic cricket dangling
in its black beak. I wondered whether the cricket was
going in or coming out, which wasn't as frivolous a con-
jecture as it might sound, for the Miracle of the Seagulls
was said to have been even more miraculous for the fact that
the birds regurgitated crickets in order to go on feeding and
save the crops of the desperate Pioneers. Alongside the
big artificial bird stood girls dressed in white cheesecloth
hung with feathers. Some day I would be a Seagull Girl.
One went up the ranks inevitably and the recurrent celebrations were like comments on Eternal Progress, the
central thread of the Gospel. I was already a Beehive Girl,
and if I had not been sitting high and important in my
sego lily today, I would have been mounted on the float

with a huge beehive in the center, wearing black and orange crepe paper with my antennae dangling.

The Priesthood Quorums of the two Wards had attended to the Indians, as usual. They had mounted a cedar on a wagon labeled "The Black Hawk Treaty Tree," and before and after this rode the Boy Scouts, painted and feathered. A white man and an Indian warrior sat on the float, facing each other, the Indian handing out the peace pipe. That had been the end of the Black Hawk War, and I knew what Chief Ungustroup had said, being already an avid reader of Indian stories, whether fictional or historical. "I, Ungustroup, have slept with treaty all night . . . I have put Mormon's shoe on my right foot, and keep Indian's moccasin on my left foot . . . we will all go down in the same trail to the creek, and our mud settle to the bottom and always be good water." Around the Treaty Tree the Gang rode, resplendent in war bonnets, their newspaper bags replaced by bows and quivers of arrows.

As our float moved into line after the one with a farmer and his plow, I kept my eyes straight ahead; some of the Indians were making war whoops and I knew Kirk was among them. I could feel the sun bearing down on my head by now; what if my curls fell out before the parade ended and I sat there covered with straggles? I looked at my toes and the shininess of my new shoes. My mouth felt stiff with smiling. As we came along the street, there was a patter of clapping, of course from the parents of the different children who were, truly, Utah's Best Crop. For children, this world In the Midst of the Mountains was a happy world.

Last of all came a long line of officials and cars bearing our town's remnant of the Pioneers who were being honored today. They followed a float depicting a desert with a cactus and then the same desert with a huge rosebush in full bloom. Around this rode horsemen and horsewomen in pairs, from the County Riding Club, resplendent in high-heeled boots and jeweled belts and silken embroidered shirts and bright, fluttering ties and broad-brimmed hats set rakishly. Superb riding horses, beautifully groomed and trained, walked proudly under these modern Westerners who looked like travel ads but were earnestly real. By the time the last of them came along the whole parade had reached the end of Main Street and had turned around upon itself. As it broke up, near the Tabernacle where the program would be held, I found the folks waiting to lift me down, and their proud faces told me it had been all right. My curls were now as fat as Mary Pickford's in "Daddy Long Legs" but could be bundled back in a ribbon for the rest of the day, leaving me free to be myself.

As we walked along the street with the crowds, people called to me how pretty I had been, and when the horses came pounding along again I could manage a glance to see whether Kirk was on one of them. And there he was, making his horse dance and turn around and around, showing off. Did he see me? I couldn't tell, for he was on his way. . . . But later, in the matinee, I heard the Gang coming in over the bedlam of paper bags bursting and balloons being deflated through their whistles and girls squealing and seats banging up and down. "Hey, I've saved you a seat!" somebody on our row yelled to somebody else who had just arrived. There were angels and flowers and bees and birds and Indians and Pioneer Children, now all melted together for the matinee which was "free to participants in the parade." I sank deep into my seat beside Carol. Soon the lights would go out. As they faded at last, the racket began to subside and the title of the comedy appeared faintly on the screen. An Our Gang comedy. But what a different gang from our gallant horsemen swaggering into a row just behind where we were sitting. The gang in the comedies was made up of engaging and innocent youngsters who imagined horses but could never have had a real one. "Shut the door! Shut the door!" we began to chant all together, toward the rear, until finally the last straggler had found a seat. And then, in the pulsing dark, I felt a hand on my shoulder. I turned. Kirk, smiling hugely, not a foot away. Blood flew to my face and I quickly faced front again. But his hand remained. "Going to the dance after?" he whispered. Not smarty at all. Just nice.

"Why—yes—" I said.

And I met his eyes again. "See you there," he said. "The first dance."

I looked raptly at the screen, not really seeing it for a while, but soon I was laughing and then, as the feature came on and developed into a great sadness, I wept quietly into my clean handkerchief. It was a love story, and I remember it well. It was about a bride who died but kept sending her ghost back to her lover. She wore her beautiful white wedding gown, and melted through a little white gate covered with roses. The beauty of her changeless love made me rapturous too, as I sat in white with my wreath of ruined flowers clutched in my hands.

The saxophone was wonderful. As usual, Carol and I lingered in the ladies' room, postponing the plunge into the absolute necessity of waiting to be asked to dance. Yet Kirk had said "the first dance," and I longed to go out at the same time that I wanted to stay among the fussing, giggling, sweet-smelling girls. I was fascinated with those a few years older than I was, especially one called Grace whom I knew my brother was sweet on. She had deep marcel waves in perfect circles running around her head and when she leaned down and lifted her skirt to adjust wide red ribbon garters, I saw her bare knees and the small, tight rolls of her stockings; on each garter was a tiny bell that tinkled as she moved out into the hall, trailing a very big silk handkerchief in her hand. Immediately she was caught up and went fox-trotting off, tinkling, laughing, red-cheeked. Red-gartered, I thought.

"Let's go," Carol said.

Kirk was not waiting. I couldn't see him at all and so I put on my not-noticing away-look and said, "I'm thirsty. Shall we get some lemonade?"

We had scarcely reached the stand when Kirk suddenly materialized in front of me. But the music had stopped. We stood awkwardly, in silence, sipping at the paper cups. And then the saxophone began its sobbing once more, and the drum said which foot to go and when to go, and the violin and piano moved melodies restlessly between. I was aware of it all, and of Kirk's shoulder rubbing my chin and his stiff legs coming against me so I had to run backwards from him, around and around. His hair was slick, separated deeply, as if the comb still rested in it and held the locks apart. He smelled nice, too, like my brother when he got dressed up, and I knew what pink oil he had bought at the drug store and how he had combed it into his hair.

That dance ended and he disappeared, but another boy came, and another. Not once did I have to slip into the dressing room to wait out a dance. I had always had to before. Every time I was alone for a minute, there was Kirk. The one time it was a slow waltz, we began to talk. But he said nothing of the box or the alphabet. He only said, "It was a swell parade, wasn't it?"

"Yes," I said. "Swell."

"Are you going to the program tonight?"

"Yes," I said again, and his tone made my heart turn over.

"With your folks?" he asked.

"And Carol." It was leading to something, I could tell. He was awkward and tense and stared out over my head. "I've got to be in the old pageant," he said. "All us Indians do. But I wondered—"

I held my breath, and sure enough he said, "I wondered if—after—we could go on the Ferris wheel or something."

Did he know I had free tickets? For a second I had this ungracious thought. But he said, "The guys in our gang got a lot of free tickets for helping put up concessions and things. I helped with the Ferris wheel and got to know the guy that runs it." He was making this talk around his waiting for my reply; it mattered to him whether I said I would meet him or not, I could see that. A feeling of prettiness swept over me like a breeze off the mountain. I even thought of something clever to say.

"My dad used to help water the elephants when the circus came to town," I said. "So he always calls helping with a carnival or something like that 'watering the elephants.'"

We laughed together. Now there was this little private family language that he shared with me.

"How about—after—" he said when the dance ended.

"I'll ask Mother."

"I'll be at the ticket booth by the Ferris wheel," he said. "As soon as I can get there, after the program."

That was the end of the dance and Carol and I went down the street together, still full of music and holiday, skipping to imaginary music. "Well, Kirk seemed to like the secret all right!" she said.

At home there was a big pitcher of punch and a plate of sandwiches and we ate sitting on the grass under the apple trees. It was Today. Today! And Tonight to come.

Kirk played the part of a wicked Indian, and I was hardly able to sympathize with the poor Pioneers, watching avidly for the coming of their enemy. I knew his horse so well that when the Pioneers had sung their evening hymns and committed their souls and bodies to the protection of Providence for the night, when their campfires were low and the scene became quiet and there was no more sound but that of a guard's plaintive guitar, I sat with my heart thumping for all the wrong reasons.

Mother said, "Sister Petersen wrote this whole pageant. All that poetry!" For now a loud, declamatory voice was announcing the fate of the sleeping Pioneers.

> "Hark, through the hush
> a sound from the brush!
> The guard, as he keeps
> his watch, half asleep,
> rouses and listens. . . ."

This is still available in the town library, and I wish somebody would put it on again. Someday, I thought that night, I too might write a pageant, having no idea that TV would have taken over the whole fiction and paralyzed the community energy by the time I got to pageant-writing age. Besides, the scholars have proved that even Westerners got their romantic ideas of pioneers and Indians from the movies and not from history. No pioneers in a train would have been silly enough to expose themselves by putting their wagons in a circle; Indians didn't actually bother them so much by fighting as by begging; and "prairie schooner" was a poetic name that never occurred to the pioneers. So even the murals were wrong. But old Sister Petersen's pageant was marvelous, all the same.

An Indian crept toward the wagons. The guard was suddenly attacked, and went down. Then, suddenly, there was a shrill cry, another, and a circle of horses were riding around and around the sleeping wagons. The pounding of their hooves was wonderful, and I could tell every time Kirk's horse passed. The circle of Indians moved like doom while the women and babies and stalwart bearded men innocently slept. High feathers blew back as the Indians rode, and they brandished bows and tomahawks over their heads. Faster and faster, and the band kept right along with them, playing something I seem to recognize every time I hear "William Tell." At last they faced the wagons, holding their bows in front of them. A cry, high and quivering, and the arrows began to fly. What a battle! Now, Kirk notwithstanding, I was loyal to the white people pouring out of the wagons in belated alarm. A red light sprang up behind the scene, the beginning of the fireworks, and we saw the Indians routed in the light of exploding rockets. Kirk's horse reared up once, excited by the explosions, and I held my breath. But he rode safely away.

We were to be permitted to stay until ten, and when the last rocket had gone off and a blazing beehive had been lighted in honor of the State of Utah and her heroic history and had fizzled out, Carol and I went off to the rendezvous as people flooded out of the grandstand to the tune of "The Star-Spangled Banner" and in the flowing light of a blazing flag. Once more we had the cheerful rhythm of the calliope and the smell of hot dogs and the shouts of concessionaires offering everything at half price for the remainder of the evening. Already a few of the stands were coming down; by dawn there would be nothing left and children could explore under the grandstand for lost handkerchiefs and prizes and balloons and sometimes even dimes and nickels that had been dropped through the cracks above. Once Carol had found fifty cents, a historic coin that all our friends envied far beyond its monetary value.

We stood at the ticket office of the Ferris wheel, waiting. My heart beat to the music as people moved in the line, got into their seats and out again, rides began and ended. And he did not come, forever and forever.

"Shall we go on it once?" Carol asked impatiently. "While we wait?"

"After all, he had to take off that costume, didn't he?" I asked.

"But we could see him from the Ferris wheel and call to him," she said.

So we got on. But it was unbearable to me just then to dangle in the air where I couldn't watch the ticket booth. Up went my heart. Down went my stomach. And at last—there he was! I saw him come to the booth with one of his friends. For a whole turn I could not catch his eye. He began to walk away. As we came down I called his name. And he looked up.

So joy began. He waited with his friend, laughing at us as we went around, and when our seat came to the little stand in its turn and was tipped down and the bar removed to permit us to get off, he called grandly, "Wait— we're going up—" and he got in with me, and Carol and his friend got into the next seat and we were on our way again. When our seat stopped at the very top, Kirk leaned forward, not even holding onto the bar, swinging dangerously. Carol began to squeal, for her partner had begun swinging their seat too. As we came down, the engineer called, "Hey, you kids, take it easy! No more of that rough stuff, see?"

We stayed on four tickets' worth. Then we went once on the merry-go-round, laughing at such kid stuff but enjoying it all the same.

Then the shooting galleries. "Good! You're really good!

I'll take you target shooting," he said, showing me exactly how to hold the gun. And presently the four of us wound proudly through the crowd. I carried my souvenir target and a kewpie doll with purple feathers. Carol had a box of chocolates and kept passing it around. And the curfew had rung long since when we went walking toward home.

We stopped for a while at Carol's gate, until the candy was gone, and then Kirk and his friend walked on with me. As we passed the bridge, I wondered whether anything would be said about the secret. Perhaps Kirk didn't know, after all. He just went on telling about the fish he had caught, how huge and wonderful they were and how hard to get. He bragged of the fences his horse could take, of how he could get a hunting license of his own pretty soon and go with his father and his big brothers to get a deer. He told about his dog and its tricks. And at my gate, which he opened like a gentleman, we stood for a while, lingering on either side. His friend walked on along, calling goodnight, and Mother rose on the porch and came halfway along the path. "Is that you, Budge?"

When I answered yes, Kirk asked, "Do your folks call you Budge all the time?"

"The kids couldn't say Virginia. They said *Budginia*," I explained, and it was fun to tell him this intimate family thing. "Helen is Lulu. When Gerry yells, we call her Go-Wild-Deena. Nobody calls anybody the right name in our family."

"I'm Kirk all the time," he said. "Is it okay if I call you Budge? I mean when nobody else is around?"

There was a future for me; from now on I would see him when nobody else was around. Right now, I discovered, he was thinking about the very next day. "You going to help water those elephant-ponies in the morning?" he asked. "I've got to be down to the grounds at six."

"The man told us seven," I said.

"If you were going at six, I could take you. Ever ride double?" he asked.

Nobody would be up; the world would be dewy and beautiful. "I can go at six if I want," I said.

It was settled for the next time, but he still leaned on the fence. "Well–see you in the morning, about a quarter of." And suddenly he reached over the pickets and took my arm in his hand. "Do you like those kissing games at the parties?" he asked.

"I don't mind." Silence came between us like a fog. And then I asked, "Do you?"

"They're okay," he said. "When you get the right girl." He was looking at the sky and not at me. "You know, I was glad about that note. The guys teased me, but I got it back. It's in my pocket. If you want it—"

So he knew. But the heat that went over me was different now. He knew but it was all right. "I'd like it back," I said, my voice unsteady.

"I told them you're my girl now and they could shut up about it," he said. "If it's okay with you, when we go to those parties—" When we played Post Office he would send me a letter, stamped. When we played Climb the Cherry Tree, I would sit on his knee. Everybody would know he was the one to walk me home.

"Maybe you could wear this," he said, and held out his hand. I felt the three leaves of his Scout pin in my hand. "I'll pin it on, I know how the jigger works." I felt the exciting fumble of his hands.

"Budge! You get in here," Mother called.

Quickly, he leaned toward me and I felt the brush of his lips on my cheek. Dozens of times I had been kissed at parties, nobody thought anything about it; everybody watched and laughed and counted the forfeits. Yet this was the first time in my life and the moon seemed to swell in the sky.

"See you." He whistled as he went down the street, and I turned as if to a slow tune and wandered along the path.

"Did you have a good time?" Mother asked. "Wasn't that Kirk?"

They were all smiling. When I went upstairs even the Lady in the Moon smiled through the screen, in the center of her magic cross.